Martha's House

Alex Nassos

Publisher: Inspiring Publishers,
P.O. Box 159, Calwell, ACT Australia 2905
Email: publishaspg@gmail.com
http://www.inspiringpublishers.com

 A catalogue record for this book is available from the National Library of Australia

National Library of Australia The Prepublication Data Service

Author: Alex Nassos
Title: Martha's House
Genre: Fiction / Adventure

Paperback ISBN: 978-1-923087-50-7

Dedicated to my mother, Sylvia,
who lived a very full, eventful, and sometimes challenging life.
Never forgotten, forever missed.

PROLOGUE

It was a warm October day, one year after I inherited Aunt Martha's home and guest house in Greece, as I was preparing to close for the winter. I was proud to have survived that long. Twelve months might not seem much of an achievement. However, what I had been through in those months was more than most endured in a lifetime. I found it hard to believe that Aunt Martha had faced similar turmoil half a century before; life was different then, or so I like to believe. Taking over this quirky little house on this marvellous Greek island had been quite a journey.

Aunt Martha never explained why she chose Hydra out of all the other Greek islands. I learned this from my mother and gleaned a bit more after visiting Aunt Martha on the island several times during my youth.

Hydra is unique. There is no other place quite like it. Not much has changed since 1959 when my aunt bought the house. While there are more houses, villas, and shops catering to tourists and affluent expatriate residents, the essence remains: walking, mule rides, or expensive red and white painted water taxis are the modes of transit. Back in 1959, the villa, which later became known as Martha's House, didn't even have mains water or electricity. Addresses in Greece's small communities often come to be recognised by the residents' names. Having lived there for fifty years, Aunt Martha's name stuck, and her house, now mine, became my Trojan Horse, her fate intertwining with mine.

PART ONE

Martha's Story

CHAPTER 1

February 1955 found Martha, along with many Brits, suffering through one of Britain's coldest winters, so severe that the army and the Royal Air Force were deployed to aid the isolated, dropping supplies to the most affected areas. Martha had had enough of the fifties' Britain, with its ration coupons and bomb sites dotting London. Nearing thirty, she had lived her teenage years through World War Two, a time that had brought her joy and sorrow. Ironically, if not for the war, Martha would likely have been confined to working in the family news agency in her hometown of Marlborough. However, at eighteen, in 1943, she joined the ATS-Auxiliary Territorial Service, where she learned to drive and maintain army vehicles and where she was assigned to transport returning servicemen. It was during one such assignment in December 1944 that Martha met Charlie.

Charlie was in his late twenties but seemed much older and cynical. War does that to people. A product of the British private school system, Charlie had enlisted and was immediately commissioned as an officer. Martha wasn't a raving beauty, but she was attractive, quite tall for the time, and slim—war and war rations do that to you too. Her hair, dark blonde in her youth and usually pulled back in a bun, turned to streaked blonde in the hot summers after moving to Greece and eventually to silver grey as she aged, giving her a stern appearance at times.

She wasn't the bubbly, carefree upper-class lass that Charlie had been used to courting before the war. But she was a lively, warm body, smartly and proudly turned out in her ATS uniform, standing by her army transport vehicle when Charlie and his contingent of wounded men of the 5th Scots Parachute Battalion disembarked at Portsmouth in December 1944. By then, Charlie had seen a lot of action in Crete, Italy, and most recently in Athens, where his battalion had been deployed following the Nazi withdrawal from Greece and amidst the Greek civil war, a brutal time with Greek fighting Greek. Initially, British troops were ordered not to interfere, but eventually, under Winston Churchill's directive, they took a more active part, helping securing Athens and dealing with the Nazi retreat to Germany, all while fighting the communist-backed resistance movements. It was a challenging time for Charlie and his battalion, with over a hundred casualties that December 1944.

Charlie yearned for something beyond war and fighting, and Martha seemed like she could fill that void in his spirit nicely. Instead of jumping in the back of the vehicle with the lads, Charlie made straight for the passenger seat next to Martha. Despite being unshaven and grubby, he was attractive, his posh accent and remaining boyish charm shining through his ironic exterior.

"So, where are you from, Martha? My guess is somewhere in the West Country?" Charlie had edged closer to Martha, stretching an arm across the back of her seat. It was his opening line. He hadn't chatted up a woman in what felt like forever. Despite her stern appearance and uniform, she still seemed youthful. "Marlborough in Wiltshire, Sir," she replied, one hand on the massive steering wheel, the other shifting the gears of the battered truck. This was a delightful surprise for Charlie, who had ties to Marlborough— specifically the renowned Marlborough College. "That's absolutely marvellous, Martha. One of my cousins went to Marlborough, and my school played rugby against them quite often. I still remember those sprawling playing fields and the Polly Tearooms on the High Street. Had many delightful afternoon teas there before the war. Last time for me was 1932, actually. Perhaps we met? And please call me Charles, or Charlie to my friends." Charlie knew very well they hadn't met in 1932—she would have been a child, if not a baby. He hoped not too young, as he had no intention of inappropriate advances. But she had to be over eighteen to be in the ATS. "Everyone in Marlborough knows Polly's. I've been there many times, Sir... I mean, Charles." What Martha didn't mention was her job at Polly Tearooms before joining the ATS. She'd donned black and white attire with a frilly apron and cap, in the fashion of the early 1900s, feeling like she was playing a role in a movie, perhaps meeting a dashing boy from Marlborough College, perhaps there for tea with his seldom-seen parents. It was pure fantasy. Yet now, in this battered truck, she found herself beside a refined young man, and she hoped he wouldn't judge her because her father had been a janitor at Marlborough College, and her mother worked in a shop. After all, they said the war blurred class lines.

Charlie's charm escalated as the journey progressed, and Martha found herself increasingly drawn to him. At his insistence, she started calling him Charlie. He probing about her pre-war life, and he shared stories about his family in Berkshire and Scotland and his posh life in Oxford, where he went to university before the war. He preferred Scotland, he said. His family had an estate in the Highlands, north of Fort William, planning to return there after the war, God willing. Martha, feeling the gap in their backgrounds, began to embellish her history, stating her father worked at Marlborough College, in what capacity she didn't know as he died when she was very young and her grief-stricken mother never talked about him. Not exactly true. Martha's father Michael a school janitor had run off with one of the school's cleaning ladies and they moved to the Isle of Wright. Her mother, she said, was a property owner, Martha and her siblings had been educated at home. All lies, with some semblance of truth. Her mother did have a shop, but it was rented and Martha had missed school a lot to look after her baby sister Marguerite when their mother had to work at the shop. She hoped it all sounded much more acceptable to Charlie than the truth and maybe he would ask to see her again, just maybe.

They conversed about everything except the prevalent death and destruction, providing a brief escape from their grim realities. Eventually, they reached Longleat House near Bath, where a temporary military hospital, primarily for American soldiers, had been established. Overcrowding at other facilities meant Charlie's wounded men were to be admitted there, while Charlie himself was on special leave due to his father's severe illness, a consequence of his fighting in the trenches during the previous "Great War." High up influence had enabled Charlie to accompany his wounded men back to England and take a leave of absence.

Unlike her usual drives, often filled with the agony of severely wounded servicemen, for Martha this journey was exhilarating and she wished it would never end. Charlie enthralled her with stories of Greece, focusing on its ancient history and magnificent sites, such as the Parthenon on top of the Acropolis of Athens, rather than the combats he had experienced. He had studied Ancient Greek and Latin at boarding school. Even his battalion had a Greek connection. Their emblem was Hipponous the slayer of monsters, riding Pegasus the Greek mythological horse with wings. Martha had spent a lot of her youth reading about Roman and Greek gods and myths when babysitting her younger sister. To her, Charlie seemed like a descendant of a Greek god, descended from Mount Olympus just for her!

After Longleat, Martha had to drive Charlie to the nearby railway station at Warminster, where he was to catch a train to Reading. From there, his father's chauffeur would take him to the family home—a sprawling estate, Martha surmised. She longed to offer to drive him all the way herself but knew it was both impossible and punishable; government property was not for personal use. Charlie, keen to see Martha again and anticipating it would be easier than trying to organise something with one of his old flames, decided to press his luck.

On that freezing December day, they arrived at Warminster. The train to London via Reading was delayed, and against her better judgment, Martha acquiesced to Charlie's suggestions to leave the army truck partly concealed behind the railway station and join him for lunch at a pub. Charlie would have preferred an hour's romp in one of the rooms upstairs, but he sensed that Martha, being unexperienced and at nineteen, she probably wasn't looking for a quickie before going their separate ways. She may have had more romantic ideas in mind. They agreed to meet again in Warminster as soon as Charlie could get away from family obligations and Martha could get some leave. Charlie didn't seem that perturbed about his father's failing health, likely due to his detached upbringing and the separate lives his family led.

CHAPTER 2

A week later, Charlie and Martha met again. Charlie had been recalled for a major offensive against EAM-ELAS in Greece and needed to return posthaste. His father was still hanging on to life, but no matter, as Charlie had to get back to his battalion quick smart.

In that same smoky, not-so-charming pub in Warminster, in one of the three upstairs rooms, Martha lost her virginity and Charlie ended his forced celibacy.

There were kisses and hugs and promises to keep in touch and "as soon as this '*damn war was over*' they would meet up and do some proper courting," Martha started writing letters immediately, daily. She never received a reply. It wasn't until two months later, after making as subtle enquiries as she could about his regiment that she discovered Charlie had been killed. On the 3rd of January 1945 to be exact, during the major offensive to retake Athens. The street-by-street battle had been successful for the British troops and the Greek government, but at the cost of more than 200 British troops killed and many more wounded. Charlie's body had remained in Greece and it was assumed he was buried there. Martha felt a huge pain in her chest when she discovered that Charlie was gone and wouldn't be coming back. She longed for him to miraculously appear, perhaps as she turned a corner somewhere or was fixing her army truck in some country lane where it had broken down yet again. In her imagination, Charlie would just appear and the day would turn out very differently. But he wasn't coming back and as much as she wished and dreamed he would, she had to face that reality. It was around the same time that Martha also discovered that she was pregnant.

Being pregnant and unmarried in 1945 was often stigmatizing, sometimes disastrous. Martha had heard the whispers and gossips in the ATS about some of the unmarried girls who had fallen pregnant after a short fling with a soldier on leave, be they British, Australian, Canadian, or American. They were treated as "fallen women," particularly those from the middle and working-class families, as if their virginity was one of the few prized assets at the time. Martha knew enough that if she went through with the pregnancy, she would have to return to her mother's home and her life and that of the little one would be difficult. If her mother would have her, that is. Many families kicked their unmarried pregnant daughters out on the street, leaving them to seek shelter in some archaic institution, where as soon as the baby was born or within six weeks, the poor babies were forcibly adopted out.

Martha made few friends in the ATS. Betty had been her closest friend. They trained together and shared a room in the lodgings they had been provided by the ATS. However, shortly after a dinner dance at the local hall frequented by American soldiers, Betty had gone back to her family in Norwich. Gossip was that she had fallen pregnant. Martha decided that contacting Betty and asking her advice would be best. Caroline, her other friend, was more mature than the rest of them but seemed very old fashioned too. Caroline's father worked at the foreign office in London and even though Martha and Caroline came from different backgrounds and parts of the country, they had quickly formed a bond, much to Betty's disdain as she was the total opposite to Caroline and always felt insecure around her. Martha had the ability to switch herself and her conversations between the two total opposite characters. Martha wanted to confide in Caroline but thought better of it. Caroline might not approve and then distance herself from Martha and her predicament.

By the time Martha reached Norwich and located Betty, who lived above her family's fish and chip shop, it was mid-March, and Martha was nearly three months pregnant. Betty was raising her baby, purportedly the result of a marriage to an American soldier killed in Italy, both untruths. Betty had no idea where her dance partner from that eventful event went and was never married. Betty wore a wedding ring to support her widow status. Martha knew the truth and sensed Betty's hesitance as she entered the small flat above the shop. The thriving fish and chips business had ensured Betty's family a decent lifestyle during the war. The dish was considered the backbone to British morale.

As soon as there were just the two of them alone in the tiny kitchen, Martha told Betty of her dilemma. Without hesitation, Betty said she had to get "rid of it." Her life would be ruined if her mother wouldn't take her in and she could forget about a getting another job after the war. Betty had considered a similar path but had withdrawn in fear. Martha was reluctant to follow Betty's advice but was under immense stress due to her pregnancy and the absence of Charlie. Also, she had been starting to bleed off and on. What Martha really wanted, even though she didn't realise it at the time, was to talk to someone and share confidences. She also needed to see a doctor and there was no way she was going back to Marlborough to see the family doctor. It was in nearby Felixstowe where Betty took Martha and the doctor was unsympathetic as he told her she could either abort the pregnancy now or wait and she would lose the baby anyway if she already hadn't. The bleeding was a sign, all was not going well.

Martha ended up with no Charlie and no Charlie's baby. Regret lingered, predominantly over the lost potential life with Charlie and their baby, a future only really envisaged by Martha during their fleeting encounter.

This unfulfilled longing prompted her, ten years later, to accept Caroline's invitation to Athens, where Caroline's husband, Laurence, was a military attaché at the British Embassy. The vivid recollections and dreams of Greece, kindled by Charlie during their passionate rendezvous in Warminster in 1944, fuelled her decision.

Martha had to resign from her secretarial job at the Ministry of Defence, a position she secured after leaving the ATS in 1949. After her adventures driving army vehicles, the ministry's work seemed extremely dull, though it paid well for the time. The post-war shortage of male workers had opened opportunities for women. However, Martha, lacking advanced education, had limited options. She self-taught typing and Pitman shorthand, and after a few stops and starts using the Imperial 55 typewriter, Martha excelled by commitment and hard work over speed. Living in London in the early 1950s had its challenges. London, predominately the East End and south of the River Thames, was dotted with bomb sites. Their use now for car parks, children's play areas, and the occasional street market. Foggy London town was really a heavily polluted London. Some winter months with a cloud inversion, breathing and seeing more than a few feet was nearly impossible. Caroline and Laurence probably had no idea that their invitation to Martha to come to Greece for a holiday had motivated her to make it a permanent move. She wasn't coming back. Ever.

CHAPTER 3

Caroline suggested Martha take the recently started Greek airline TAE to Athens. Martha did some research and after visiting Thomas Cook on Fleet Street, decided against travelling on the rumoured failing Greek airline, for cost reasons more than anything else. TAE was eventually taken over by Aristotle Onassis in 1956 and became Olympic Airways in 1957, one of the most luxurious airlines at the time with air hostess dressed by Pierre Cardin.

Instead, the Thomas Cook travel agent planned a rail journey for her that would take in Paris, Geneva, Milan, Vienna, Belgrade, and finally, Thessaloniki and Athens. Martha had rarely smiled since February 1945, but she had problems controlling some excitement at the thought of the journey ahead of her. Only ten years before, Europe had been gripped in a most dreadful war and now she was travelling across the Continent by train, and according to Thomas Cook, experiencing a journey of a lifetime.

The journey took seven days travelling Second Class, sharing a four-bed couchette with different people that came and went as she crossed Europe. The most delightful morning was when she woke early on her top bunk and lifted a small part of the window blind to be confronted with the most outstanding view of the Swiss Alps, still covered in snow in the April sunshine.

Martha observed the train engine and conductors were replaced at each country's border. Not such a big deal until the train reached the Austrian Yugoslav border and the Austrian train engine was replaced by the oldest, slowest most dirty smoking engine imaginable. So bad that everyone was told to keep their windows closed, or to suffer themselves and their belongings being covered in black soot. Luckily, there was an Italian businessman in the next compartment who had travelled the route many times. He had warned them to get out at Vienna station and quickly stock up on water and bread as there would be no restaurant carriage through Yugoslavia, even drinking water was questionable. All the joy Martha felt travelling across Europe melted when they hit Yugoslavia. In addition to the lack of food and water, the train travelled at a snail's pace, most of what could be seen outside the carriage window was miserable and still showed signs of war. More often than necessary, particularly in the dead of the night, the train would stop in the middle of nowhere and badly dressed armed guards would board demanding passports and papers.

Martha had been warned by seasoned travellers not to leave her handbag and valuables in easily accessible places, as the main objective of these midnight boardings was to collect bribes and pilfer whatever was easily available. Some of the midnight raiders were real police, many not, but looked the part. Desperate people do desperate things. Another fallout of war and poverty. The highlight at the time was Zagreb, which resembled the grandeur of Vienna or Budapest more than the rest of the country.

Once they reached the Greek border on the seventh day, Martha was quite exhausted, with little sleep and stressed from the previous two days' journey. Within an hour, the atmosphere changed from dismal to delightful! A new engine was attached to the train. Not as fancy as the Swiss, but a huge improvement over the Yugoslavian one. The running of the train was handed over to the Greek conductors, and the Greek border police came on board to do their passport checks. Lots of smiles and "welcome to Greece" greetings! After some more train shunting, a glamourous dining carriage was added to the rear of the train. Menus were handed out to both first and second class and everyone encouraged to take lunch or dinner in the train dining room, and some wine or ouzo to get into the Greek way of life.

Martha hadn't eaten in any of the dining carriages on the journey so far, fearing the cost. However, this arrival in Greece had to be celebrated. Washed as best she could in the carriage wash basin and changed into lighter clothes as the temperature had risen considerably, she set off for her first proper meal in a week. She was greeted by smiling, smartly dressed waiters in uniforms and bow ties. Lunch tasted incredible. She wasn't sure what she ordered or what was served but was told it was good Greek food, and it was delicious. Later, she realised it was an oven-baked pasta dish and a basic Greek salad of tomatoes and feta cheese, all drenched in olive oil. Martha had never tasted olive oil before; she had only seen it at chemists in England, in tiny bottles, prescribed for ear problems. Here, the olive oil was almost green in colour and eaten just with Greek bread, which also tasted very different but lovely, a meal in itself.

Sitting in the dining car and enjoying her lunch and the attention of the waiters, the train arrived at Thessaloniki, Greece's second largest city. Martha caught vistas of the hustle and bustle of a thriving city built around its iconic White Tower and her first glimpse of the blue Mediterranean Sea. To the distance overlooking the city was the castle fortress Heptapyrgion, "seven towers" in English; it actually has ten towers, but Martha wasn't counting. Everything seemed so exotic and wonderful. A few hours later, still in the dining car and now savouring her first taste of ouzo, one of waiters came by and told her to look out the opposite window. Mount Olympus had come into view. Martha was taken back to her short but most memorable time with Charlie and his tales of Greece. In some way, she felt that at the end of this journey, Charlie would be waiting for her, here in the land of the gods.

A few of her fellow long-distance travelling companions had disembarked in Thessaloniki and her compartment now felt less crowded, with just one other traveller, a French lady who had boarded in Paris. Martha would have been quite happy if this part of the journey went on for another week or even longer. However, too soon, it was very late in the evening when they reached their final destination. Martha collected all her belongings, including a jolly painted biscuit tin of what remained of the shortbread biscuits she had brought with her from London—a farewell gift from her mother, a possession she would never part with her whole life. It was the last remanant of her old life and would serve a purpose in her new one.

There on the platform was a happy, tanned Caroline, exuberant that her friend from the ATS days had finally arrived.

CHAPTER 4

By 1956, Martha had been in Athens for nearly a year. Through Laurence, Martha had secured a job at the British Embassy processing visa applications, import and export permits, and assisting in getting documents notarised. She didn't feel uncomfortable using Laurence to get the job. After all, it was because of Martha that he met Caroline when she was waiting outside the entrance of the Ministry of Defence in London for Martha to finish work so they could go for tea. It had been love at first sight between Caroline and Laurence, leaving Martha with no choice but to invite Laurence to Lyons Corner House in Piccadilly, where they were headed. At least he picked up the bill, but he could afford it as even then he held quite a senior position in the Ministry. Who could have imagined that just a couple of years later they all three would end up living in Athens.

Despite the ravages of the war ten years prior and the Greek civil war until 1949, Athens had retained its dignity. There was an aura of people enjoying themselves, whether out drinking and eating at the many cafés and tavernas or enjoying the many beaches along the Attica coastline from Faliron to Vouliagmeni. Politics continued to play a major role in every Greek's life, and division over politics—a fallout of the civil war—persisted, continuing even to this day.

Most of the city consisted of white-painted, two-level homes with flat roofs. Children were often seeing playing, moving across whole streets by jumping from roof to roof. Greece was returning to a new norm, and food, scarce during the war when more than 100,000 died in Athens alone from starvation, was now in better supply than in Britain. So much so that overeating and overordering at tavernas seemed to have become a fashion.

After a short period living with Caroline, Laurence and their two small children near the British Embassy in Kolonaki, one of the most expensive areas of Athens, Martha moved into a room in a neoclassical house in Plaka. This was the old part of the city, rather rundown in those days but very central, graced and overshadowed by the Acropolis. Mr Yannis and his wife, Sofia, were in their late seventies. Their only child, also Sofia, had left many years before for Boston in America and had married into a Greek American family. Their dream was to travel to Boston to see Sofia and the grandchildren they had only known by letter and photographs. The war and the following civil war had so far prevented them. Renting out a room to a foreigner, one that worked at an embassy, gave them the extra drachmas they needed. For Martha, it was perfect. She had a large room at the top of the house, where Yannis and Sofia couldn't easily access anymore. Her view was of the Acropolis of Athens and Sofia didn't speak English. Yannis did, and also French, but he didn't talk much anymore. Martha was compelled, rather than forced, to learn Greek to communicate as she really wanted to learn the language. There was little opportunity to do that at the Embassy as all communication was in English. Within six months, Martha was having conversations in Greek and could even get by reading the Greek newspapers. Compared to Pitman shorthand, she thought, it was less challenging and much more interesting.

Martha loved living in Athens. One most memorable winter day occurred when she and three others from the embassy decided to spend their Sunday walking up to the Acropolis and exploring the Parthenon and other temples before walking back down to the flea market in Monistiraki and having lunch in an old taverna in Plaka. Exploring the Acropolis, Martha felt close to Charlie again, remembering his exuberant description of this ancient monument towering above the city. That day stayed with Martha for a long time, and the photograph of her and her colleagues in front of the Parthenon took pride of place when she eventually settled into her own home.

The only fly in the ointment during those wonderful days in Athens was the conflict in Cyprus, a British protectorate at the time. There was growing passion to kick out the British and return Cyprus to independence and build closer ties to republicans in Greece. There were many closed-door discussions at the British Embassy, and Laurence seemed to be at the heart of it all. The tragic events during May 1956 in Athens marked another turning point in Martha's life. Martha was crossing Syntagma Square on her way to the British Embassy when she found herself in the middle of a major demonstration. Demonstrators collided with police, shots were fired, and unarmed people died in the resulting tumultuous aftermath. Martha saw bodies lying where they fell, in front of the Royal Palace and near the Grande Bretagne hotel. She always imagined that Charlie had been killed more or less in the same spot. Often, as she walked past the Grande Bretagne on her way to the embassy, she would run her hands on its majestic walls, trying to feel Charlie's spirit.

Martha managed to get through the crowds to the safety of the Embassy. However, even there, a fear of attack from demonstrators prevailed. Martha learned that this was because two Cypriots were being executed for being members of the outlawed Cypriot EOKA independence movement, having been found guilty of participating, directly or indirectly, in the killing of policemen and two British soldiers. Many Greeks had come out in support of Cypriot independence and against the execution.

Martha hadn't moved to Greece to be confronted with even more death and destruction. Selfish as it felt, she had her fill during the war. She wanted the romantic Greece that Charlie described to her. She wanted to walk in history with Charlie. So far, she had only found his name at the Commonwealth War Memorial in Faliron, overlooking the sea to the south of Athens city centre. She had visited the war memorial that very day to lay flowers and talk to him in her own special way, before taking a bus back to Syntagma and getting caught up in the deadly demonstration. As much as she didn't want to leave Charlie, even if he was just a name on a memorial amongst 3,000 others, Martha yearned to discover more of Greece and find herself. A few days prior, at one of the many Embassy social events, this time at the nearby American Embassy, there had been much talk of Hollywood coming to Greece to film an epic called *Boy on a Dolphin*, starring the famous American actor Alan Ladd and the recently discovered Italian beauty Sophia Loren. The filming was mostly to take place on the island of Hydra. Talk of Hydra bounced around the social crowd in the Embassy gardens. Martha learned that Hydra was a place with no cars and few modern conveniences, yet many artists lived there. Quite a few of them expatriates. It was the latest vogue destination for Greek-loving foreigners who spent their days painting the incredible scenery, drinking, eating, laughing, and engaging in all sorts of debauchery. Martha was fascinated. She had never totally fit in anywhere. Was there really a place that sounded to her like a modern-day Mount Olympus, where a person, even as different as her, with a past she didn't want to share with anyone, could go and just be herself or even create a new persona, as she did when she met Charlie?

CHAPTER 5

By coincidence, or was it providence, her landlords, Yannis and Sofia had a house on Hydra. They hadn't been there for many years, even before the war. Sofia had inherited the place, which had passed down through generations. As far as they knew, it was habitable but nothing special. Even if they wanted to, there was no way they could get there in their condition. It was high up with more than 200 steps, they told Martha, but she was free to go and stay there as often as she liked.

As soon as Martha had a free weekend from work, she organised her trip to Hydra. It was a three-hour ferry journey from Piraeus. The ferry made a few stops on the way: Aegina, then Poros, and finally Hydra. Martha stood outside on the ferry all the way there. She wanted to take in all the sights and stops. Every island had that Greek charm but was different. After leaving Poros, the ferry steamed round the headland jutting out from the mainland of the Peloponnese and turned south; she could see quite a large, rocky, barren island to the head of her coming up on the port side. Even from this vista, Hydra looked amazing and proud. From this viewpoint, the only buildings looked like monasteries. Then more buildings appeared, built precariously overlooking the sea. Suddenly, the ferry turned sharp port side and entered Hydra port. The previously hidden view coming into the amphitheatre of the harbour was breathtaking.

The actors and film crews of *Boy on a Dolphin* had left months before, and Hydra had gone back to being its quiet, solidly unchanging, and unbendable old self. Mules and mule men in baggy trousers, checked shirts, and drooping moustaches dominated the social scene. There was a smattering of foreigners—writers, artists, and drunks. Some were all three. A mule man, familiar with Yannis and Sofia's house, took her there for a few drachmas. Martha wanted to walk, but he insisted she ride the mule while he led.

This was the first of many visits Martha would make to Hydra. Eventually, in 1959 she had saved enough money to buy Yannis and Sofia's house on the island. They were only too happy to sell, as they were getting desperate to go to America to see their daughter and grandchildren. As soon as they had saved what they thought was enough, the cost of the sea journey to America had risen. It was very frustrating for them, and they worried they would die before they managed to get to Boston. They had no intention of selling their house in Plaka; it had been bequeathed to their daughter, Sofia, as part of her wedding dowry. They hoped one day their daughter or grandchildren might want to come and stay there.

For the first time in her life, buying the house on Hydra made Martha feel she was truly independent and wouldn't have to rely on anyone for anything anymore. She could be herself on that island, whatever that was. For the next few years, Martha travelled back and forth between her job at the Embassy in Athens and Hydra. She had built up a circle of people through the embassy who would gladly go and rent a room in her Hydra home for weekends and holidays. The extra money she earned enabled her to make some improvements to the property and also pay for her own ferry tickets.

Martha preferred to have little to do with the other foreigners that lived on the island in the 1950s and early 1960s. Most of them lived in the arty world and had come from money. Even those that were now broke exuded an air of confidence and achievement that made Martha feel slightly inferior. She had seen them spending way too much time at some of the tavernas, particularly Douskos Taverna—drinking, eating, dancing, and thoroughly enjoying themselves. Martha preferred to spend her Hydra time in her small garden, tending to her lemon trees and bougainvillaea, or going to one of the secluded stony beaches for a swim in the summer months and sipping Greek coffee whilst reading a book at one of the quieter cafés around the port.

Her escapism on Hydra started to be interrupted once word got around that she worked at the British Embassy and she spoke Greek. Soon, one expatriate after another would come to her asking for help with some local bureaucratic problem they were having, or perhaps assistance with visas. Every time, she politely turned them and their party invitations down, explaining that, as an employee at the British Embassy, she was less able to interfere in local issues than anyone else. Eventually, most gave up and left her in peace. Martha felt differently when locals approached her, asking for advice and help on how they could send their children to England to attend a college or university. Even though many on the island lived on very little, most owned their house, passed down through generations or obtained through a marriage, and their first priority was to ensure that their children had a better life and more opportunities. Many young men found work as seamen on Greek ships, with Greek shipping becoming dominant in global sea transportation. Greeks from many islands had capitalised on opportunities in post-war shipping, creating many multi-millionaires. Onassis, a regular visitor to Hydra, was just one of many, arriving on his superyacht, *Christina*, and later in the 1960s, bringing Jacqueline with him. Martha had seen them once or twice. They moved in a world very different from Martha's. The Onassis brigade would bring out many of the local expats who would want to grab one of the tables near them, at whichever taverna they were at or what was then the

Hydra Yacht Club, if at least to say they were there at that time with Jacqueline, hoping to be invited to join them at their table.

Martha, however, kept to herself. Her main contacts were Despina, the housekeeper she had inherited from Yannis and Sofia; the local mayor, Andreas; and his lawyer, Stellios. Despina worked at quite a few houses on Hydra, many belonging to wealthy Athenians, and some rented by foreigners who had settled on the island. Through Despina, Martha kept up with the local gossip and who was having an affair with whom amongst the arty world, so distinct from the world of the Hydriots. Of course, the latter too had their pre-marriage affairs and matrimonial flings, typically kept quiet, with most attending church on Sundays as if the communion bread wouldn't melt in their mouths.

The local mayor would often seek her out, believing somewhat naively that her position at the British Embassy would be something that could carry some weight should he need help in that direction. He introduced her to his lawyer, Stellios Condos, and Martha engaged him to handle any bureaucratic problems she occasionally encountered with her house.

Condos fell in love with Martha instantly. His wife lived in Athens and rarely, if ever, visited the island. Condos found more excuses than any normal person would think possible to see Martha, whether she was in Athens or Hydra. His feelings were not reciprocated, but Martha retained him as her lawyer. Just about everyone in Greece had a lawyer; it was like having a doctor anywhere else.

CHAPTER 6

Condos had made Martha think that perhaps she should get a lover. Maybe that would put Condos in his place. She was determined never to marry; Charlie had been her first and only, irreplaceable love. Still, she was of a reasonable age, thirty-five by now, and that's when she met Manolis.

She had seen him around Hydra a few times during holidays. She assumed he had a house there but didn't live on the island year-round. He was of average height and had a smart look about him, projecting accomplishment and wealth, with his immaculately pressed, expensive-looking clothes. He had black hair, sliver at the edges, and hands that didn't appear to belong to one of the local mule drivers.

One day, while sitting at her favourite café on the port, Manolis came and sat at the table next to hers. He focused on his newspaper, and she was deep into her Agatha Christie novel. Martha ordered her usual Greek coffee, *metrio*, medium sweet, and Manolis ordered his usual Greek coffee, *varyglyko*, very sweet. Whether it was deliberate or not, Spyros, their waiter, managed to get their orders mixed up. Something he had never done before. Manolis was the first to take a sip and immediately recognised that his wasn't his usual brew. Then Martha tasted hers and almost spat out the overly sweet, thick coffee that you could stand a spoon in.

They then both turned and looked at each other. Manolis was the first to speak. "My dear, I believe that our loyal waiter Spyros has given me your coffee and you mine," he said in perfect English. Martha nodded in agreement, as she gulped down the obligatory glass of water one always gets with a Greek coffee. When she recovered, she allowed herself, for the first time in nearly twenty years, to engage in an almost flirtatious conversation, this time with this Greek stranger. He said he had seen her on Hydra a few times before and then at one of the garden parties the British commercial attaché had organised at the Embassy. He had just finished his conversation with the Ambassador and had turned to seek her out when she had vanished. And here they were now, finally with their correct coffee orders, sitting in the wonderful spring sunshine on Hydra. He wasn't Charlie, but he was charming. He pointed out his house behind the island KEP, the local citizen service centre which provided many services to locals and expats. It was one of the mansions Martha had admired every time she sailed into the harbour. Manolis's mansion faced southwest, catching much of the day's sun and offering fantastic sunsets. Great in the cooler months, but darned hot in summer. The ceilings looked enormous, as did the grey-painted windows in the sandstone brick façade. She had learned that a wealthy shipowner owned the place and it was only occupied occasionally. She wondered if Manolis was really the owner or if he was the caretaker.

CHAPTER 7

T he "coffee swap," as they both came to call it, turned out to be a fortunate turn of events, Martha decided. Despina confirmed that he was indeed the shipowner who owned the mansion and that he was married with a son and a daughter—facts he didn't hide from Martha when she broached the subject as diplomatically as possible. Manolis wasn't going to come up with white lies. His wife preferred to spend her time and his money in Monaco, visiting Athens a few times of the year and never came to Hydra as she didn't like sea journeys, even though married to a ship owner, and she certainly wouldn't walk or ride a mule up the steep steps to the house on Hydra that Manolis's family had owned for generations. His children were both at school; his daughter with her mother in Monaco and his son Mihali was at a private French school in Athens. Mihali was destined to take over the family business one day, and if it all turned out, even though he was only about four years old at the time, he would marry another shipowner's daughter, and so their fortunes and fleets would be enlarged.

Martha doubted that Manolis would be talking to her if she wasn't working at the embassy. Even though she was one of the lowest-ranking employees there and a local hire, rather than a diplomatic appointee from London, the Greeks she met seemed to hold her in some esteem.

They started to meet up for coffee every time Manolis came to Hydra. It was fairly simple for Manolis to get to and from Hydra. His visits started to increase, especially since his company headquarters—operationally, at least, as his ships were all under some flag of convenience—were in Piraeus, overlooking the port. Things never went further than coffee until Martha mentioned that after ten years, she was planning to go to England the next month. Her mother had passed away, and even though she hadn't made the funeral, her sister Marguerite had been pressing her to come back for ages so that Martha could also attend her niece's christening, where Martha was to be the godmother. Surprise, surprise, Manolis was going to London too, and he said that he would organise a ticket for her to fly on Onassis's airline, Olympic Airways, and they could meet up afterwards in London, where he kept an apartment just off Park Lane. Martha wasn't naive; she knew what the invitation really meant. She said she would think about it. She didn't think long, and ten days later when they met up again for morning coffee, Martha accepted the invitation.

A few weeks later, Martha was at Athens International Airport in Ellinikon on the outskirts of Athens. Sure enough, there was a ticket waiting for her at the Olympic Airways desk, and she was escorted to the first-class lounge as if she was a film star. Her flight to London was on a De Havilland Comet. Some ten years prior, she had taken seven days to get to Athens by train in second class. Now she was going back on an aeroplane in first class that would take five hours. She convinced herself that she wasn't going to get used to this sort of travel; the price was an affair with Manolis, and who knows if that would last. She liked the man and enjoyed his company, but she wasn't in love, and didn't think he was either. He had many homes around the world, and even though he was at least twenty years older than her, he probably had mistresses in each of them. Martha certainly would not be sharing any of this with her family, not that they had been close in any case.

CHAPTER 8

Marlborough was much the same as it had been since Martha had last visited ten years before. One difference was that her mother's news agency was now a bookshop, run by her sister Marguerite and her husband, Matthew. Matthew had been a travelling salesman selling Encyclopaedia Britannica books when he called at Marguerite's family home. They started dating soon after and were married within a year. It was Matthew who convinced Marguerite to turn the news agency into a proper book shop. Martha discovered that owning a bookshop had elevated her little sister up the social ladder in Marlborough, and the shop was becoming a destination for visitors to the area. The other surprise for Martha was meeting her niece, Zoe, for the first time. "Thank goodness," she thought, "not another M in the Miller family." Zoe was a cute little thing. She had just started walking and took to her Aunt Martha immediately. As much as Martha wanted to remain standoffish, she did warm up to Zoe, a little anyway. The christening had been organised in the local church, St Mary's, and to Marguerite's dismay as soon as it was over Martha said she had to leave for London.

Manolis had everything organised. He had given Martha instructions to meet him for dinner at Rules near Covent Garden. He had booked a room at the Hilton Hotel on Park Lane. He certainly wouldn't be going to his apartment nearby, nor to the Dorchester where he was well known. Martha just had something that intrigued him. She wasn't the most beautiful woman he had met. Maybe it was the way she always presented that British stiffness and coldness that made him what to tear down the walls she had built around her. It would be a conquest indeed, and he liked a challenge. He wouldn't be where he was now without destroying the barriers in his path from starting out as ship's officer to becoming a shipowner. Manolis did not have entirely clean hands; he seized an opportunity to do a deal with Iranians he had met on his many sea voyages in and out of Bandar Abbas. The Iranian oil embargo of the early 1950s was an opportunity, and he had grasped it, chartering ships, switching flags of convenience, and transporting shipments. From chartering ships, he soon had enough to start buying his own and bringing in other investors. In ten years, he had built up a fleet of over fifty ships, tankers, and bulk carriers. Unlike some of the Greek shipowners, he wasn't reliant on American banks and so was comfortable operating legitimate and, on some occasions, opportunistic business. He had a team of managers running the business, under his control of course. Most of the senior positions were Manolis's relatives. Family was important then and now. He had to be in control and he revelled in dominating people, as he would Martha very, very soon.

Martha reluctantly, yet thoroughly enjoyed her steak at Rules. She had gotten used to a mostly vegetarian diet in Greece, interspersed with chicken and the occasional lamb usually at Greek Easter. It was the first time she had tasted fillet steak, and with the red wine Manolis lavished on her, she was soon feeling warm and rather heady. She couldn't help thinking what the evening would have been like had it been with Charlie. She couldn't recall Charlie being as abrupt and demanding as Manolis was. He was obviously well known in the place, and the huge tip he left on the way out must have made the staff feel it was worth putting up with his arrogance.

Manolis suggested they walk to Park Lane and have a drink at the Hilton Hotel, which had only opened a few years before. It was all very glamorous to her, but inside left her cold. She would rather be sitting in a café in Athens or Hydra, with a good book. But here she was, and she thought maybe she would enjoy the evening after all. How bad could it be? When they got to the Hilton, Manolis manoeuvred Martha straight to the elevators and up to the suite he had booked, overlooking Hyde Park. The door had barely shut behind them when he got straight into pushing her up against the wall and kissing her like a drowning man. She just went along with it; many years had passed since her last with a man and she still had thoughts of maybe getting pregnant, married or not, she was going to try and have a baby this time.

The night was very different for her. Her only previous experience was that one time with Charlie many years before. Manolis was very passionate, but it was just sex for both of them. Once was enough for her, but after about an hour he wanted more and he wanted it differently. For Martha, it was too much and too soon and she told him. She could feel his disappointment and Manolis could sense her walls coming back up. He wasn't going to give up; this little interlude might have to go on further as he wanted to break her in a way, wanted her pining after him. And then he would probably lose interest, as he always did. But she was never going to succumb to his or anyone's control. Now matter how many first-class trips on aeroplanes and steak dinners he offered.

CHAPTER 9

Martha enjoyed being back on Hydra. Her trip to London was an experience; that's all she could say about it. She still wasn't pregnant despite meeting up with Manolis again a few times in Athens, never on Hydra as too many people would know. She realised that the colder she was with him in bed, the more excited he got. If she gave him disdaining looks as well, it was like an aphrodisiac to Manolis.

It was after Manolis that she took another lover, a French one this time. Michel worked at the French embassy in Athens and, through the diplomatic social events, had learnt of Martha's House on Hydra and came as a paying guest for a long weekend. Michel was very charming, very considerate, and extremely polite. Being with Michel wiped memories of Manolis in bed, and that was good. There were a few more lovers after that for Martha, each one wiping the memories of the previous. She had come to the conclusion that she was never going to have children; that trip to the doctor in Felixstowe back in 1945 must have ended any chance of motherhood. But she had her niece Zoe and her cats now, who were even more important to Martha, and that was absolutely fine.

Her relationship with Manolis continued, off and on, until Zoe came to visit one summer. Zoe had turned into quite a pretty teenager and her mother had written to Martha asking if she could come and spend the summer with her on Hydra. "She is attracting too much boy attention," Marguerite wrote, "I want her to finish her education and do something with her life, not just get married and have babies." Martha, for once, agreed with her sister.

It didn't take long for Zoe to get in with the local teenage crowd on Hydra. Most of her newfound friends were either half Greek and half something else, or were children of foreigners who had houses on Hydra and there just for the summer. Martha wasn't experienced in looking after adolescents and just let Zoe go off every day and do whatever young people do on Hydra during the summer. There didn't seem to be any problem, until one evening when she was sitting on her terrace reading yet another crime novel. The door to the street flung open and a red-faced, red-nosed Zoe came in and, unlike her usually exuberant funny self, said she was off to bed and good night. The next morning, Martha went down for a coffee at her café, sitting in her usual spot when she saw Manolis walking very purposely straight towards her.

"I had to have words with your niece last night," he said. "She has been hanging around with the crowd my son Mihali keeps company with and trying to seduce him; she turned up at my house for goodness' sake. Mihali is a serious boy, He has to study for his final exams this year for university. I didn't mind them being in the same company as he needs to practice his English, but he has become besotted with your niece and enough is enough. She should know her place, and it's not near my son, and not visiting him in my house!"

Martha was completely taken aback. Was this the same charming man she had now known for quite a few years and, even though they weren't lovers anymore, she thought they had a friendship? Martha wasn't one to back down, even with the local highflyer. Very slowly she removed the enormous sunglasses she wore, which had become her trademark on the island, stood up, and looked him straight in the eye. "So my niece is good enough to help your son practice his

English but not good enough to keep company with him, or be let into your house, which she wouldn't have done uninvited?"

Martha wasn't going to wait for a response; she went on, "Is that because she, and me for that matter, are not in your class?"

Manolis was silenced for a second or two; no one spoke back to him especially when he was in temper. Most ran away, hid, cowered. "He has gone back to Athens anyway, first ferry this morning." It was the only thing he could think of telling Martha.

Martha turned to walk away back to her house, furious. "And you, Manolis, have just talked your way out of my life as I realise now that you are just not good enough for me, not even as a so-called friend. I hope you have found that your English has improved too since you met me, because your manners certainly haven't." Those were the last words she spoke to him, ever.

Zoe was up when Martha got back to the house. The incident had in some way made her feel closer to her niece. All Martha said was that she had bumped into Mihali's father in the port and he said his son had gone back to Athens. Nothing more was offered up by either of them. After a day, Zoe went off again, this time on a trek to Lemonitza on the other side of the island, with the young Hydra crowd, which now didn't include Manolis's son.

After that, Martha's niece came a few times to Hydra, not often and not for long; Zoe was always on her way to somewhere. Martha hoped that one day Zoe would stop being such a gypsy and find a place she enjoyed spending more than a few days. Often you don't realise it, sometimes the best things are right there in front of you.

PART TWO

Zoe's Story

CHAPTER 10

Most of my relatives' names begin with the letter M: my mother Marguerite, my father Matthew, and my mother's sister Martha. To the extent that my parents both shared the same surname of Miller, even before marriage. This is compounded by us also living in a small country town in England called Marlborough. My mother decided there were enough 'Ms' in the Miller family and opted to name her children with the last letter of the alphabet. So, I was named Zoe and my younger brother Zac.

My aunt Martha had already relocated to Greece before I was born and had evolved into a fully committed philhellene. I theorise that my mother, bless her, had a cunning plan in naming me Zoe, which is, of course, a name of Greek origin meaning life. The Greeks pronounce it more like Zoeee... My aunt Martha was also my godmother. My mother probably anticipated that giving me a Greek name and making her sister my godmother would angle me as Aunt Martha's beneficiary. My brother Zac wasn't included in the cunning plan. Mother foresaw Zac standing on his own two feet, getting married, having a family, and taking over the family bookshop in the small country town where I grew up and where the family still lived. Whereas I, little Zoe, was perceived as more likely to end up as a spinster, just because I was more into reading books than selling them and considered myself very independent, in thought at least. The significant dependency was that Aunt Martha would not marry, have children of her own, adopt, or acquire stepchildren. It seemed a long shot, but my mother must have known a hell of a lot more about her sister Martha than she let on to the rest of the family. I learnt more about Aunt Martha after I moved to Greece then I ever did from my mother.

After two hip replacements in a hospital in Piraeus, Martha decided she wanted to return to England after fifty years on Hydra, back to her birthplace. Most people count what they do in one or two years, but not here; decades pass before you know it. People in Greece tend to live longer, but not as long as the Japanese, I think. That is if they don't smoke themselves to death or fall victim to the numerous Greek road casualties every year. No chance of being run over on Hydra. There are no cars. Not even bicycles. They're banned. Aunt Martha didn't smoke, didn't drive a car anymore anyway, and being generally of good health, she had reached the age of eighty-seven and, I assumed, decided she wanted a life change. Leaving Hydra with few possessions, she made it as far as Athens. Apparently, shortly after meeting with her lawyer to finalise her last will and testament, she left this world entirely whilst sitting on an old friend's terrace, looking up at the Acropolis from an apartment in the Plaka district of Athens. I believe she never really actually wanted to leave Greece and passed away in a happy and peaceful way.

Still, Aunt Martha leaving the house to me was surprising. She always said everything was going to her cats—the colony that lived at the back of Martha's House—to be managed by the local Hydra cat charity, Ark. Indeed, the main stipulation of her legacy to me was that I had to ensure that Auntie's cat colony was taken care of. Additionally, I had to participate in the annual cat round-up, when visiting veterinarians from Athens would neuter and tend to the cats who had vey reluctantly been captured for the event. Ensuring my tetanus jabs were up to date was imperative.

It had always been my dream to spend at least six months of every year in the sun, far away from the urban jungle and damp weather. Dreams aside, I never thought I would leave my city life—until, that is, I got the telephone call from Athens. Mr Condos, Aunt Martha's somewhat shady lawyer, had taken over looking after her affairs from his father. The older Mr. Condos had catered to Aunt Martha's legal needs ever since she landed on the island back in the 1950s. I think she chose him was because he was also the lawyer for the then local mayor, who had a finger in every pie imaginable. She likely concluded that if Mr Condos Senior could keep a mayor out of jail, if needed, then he must be good. And so, I ended up with shady lawyer Mr Stelios Condos Junior.

I fantasised about moving to a totally different place, just like Aunt Martha had done in 1955 when she set off by train from London to Athens. I always loved travelling; every time I went somewhere, I would assess if I could live there. After a week, sometimes days, I would move on. Aunt Martha used to call me a gypsy.

I would never have permanently stepped out of my city dweller comfort zone, holidaying in far-off places whenever I could, if it hadn't been for that telephone call. The call made the decision for me. I certainly wasn't brave enough to make permanent decisions—not as brave Aunt Martha, that's for sure.

I dreamed of living out my days in the sun somewhere. But I knew that unless I could also earn a living, I wouldn't survive, financially speaking. Worse still, I could become your typical inebriated expat, which I wasn't inclined to do willingly—not yet, anyway. Just give me a few years, and that might change, too. Wherever this perfect life change was, I needed to be able to make enough money to pay the bills. I wasn't cashed up enough to go somewhere and spend my days hanging around cafés and bars, growing wrinkled under a hot sun and dry wind. Aunt Martha, in her wisdom, had picked up on that as well.

That was before destiny led me to this island, Hydra, a place where I had always loved to spend holidays with Aunt Martha but never thought I could afford to live. These days you can buy property in the best suburbs of Athens cheaper than on Hydra. Even with the financial crises unfolding around me, I had concluded that no one here on this island really wanted to sell. Many of the hundred-odd foreign residents on the island—displaying various degrees of oddity—occasionally wallow in a desire to sell up and move to some other crazy, equally romantic location. They too have atmospheric expectations of what they believe their property is worth. The old adage that everything is only worth what someone wants to pay for it doesn't apply to Hydra. Here, you put a silly price on your house and wait for another silly person to come along, however long that may take. Time is not an issue on Hydra.

Aunt Martha always struck me as a bit odd too. Why else would you go and live on a small island, surround yourself with indifferent locals—some as kind as heavenly possible and others downright evil. I had one such very unpleasant encounter when I was fifteen, spending the summer on the island. More about that later, and my run-in with Auntie's friend Manolis. And let's not forget the non-locals who choose to come and live here, leaving so-called civilised cities like Paris, New York, Vienna, to name a few, far behind, each with their own sack of raisons d'être. Nearly everyone is a painter or writer, trying to recreate the bohemian days on the 1950s and 1960s when Hydra was also a mecca for artists seeking creativity and like-minded companions. The fact that today few have actually sold a painting for money, or had a book published other than at their own expense, doesn't prevent them from donning their homemade cloak of the "mysterious artist" when they meet a new arrival on the island. Yes, I have met many "artists" on Hydra in the short time I have been here since Aunt Martha forced my hand.

Maybe there was some of the adventurous and eccentric Aunt Martha in me after all. Not that I would flatter myself to have attained the levels she achieved when she moved to Greece nearly fifty years before. My reality, when taking over Martha's House was that my life had progressed to standing on the edge of a precipice with a deadly vertical descent on the other side, which in hindsight necessitated a very large and robust parachute.

CHAPTER 11

I t had taken me four days to get here from London. What a trip that was! A friend's Ford Transit was our vehicle, driven by him as a huge favour, packed with my furniture and prized personal objects that I just couldn't bear to part with. The truck was jam-packed so tight with a mountain of bits and bobs so full that not even the Swiss border control dared delve too far in.

Taking over a hotel—or more of a guest house—on a Greek island didn't seem like enough adventure for me. Forced into that first step, I briefly felt like an adventure addict; I craved more! I opted not to take the uncomplicated route, letting some transport company move me lock, stock, and kitchen table. Instead, I thought, why not get a friend who has a truck and is heading that way to drive me across Europe down to Ancona in Italy, then book the ferry across to Greece and have a bit of a laugh on the way?

I had already researched that the only way to get my worldly possessions to Martha's House from the mainland opposite the island was to have them transported on that last leg of the journey by some sort of barge or local ferry, then brought up the hill by mule. Regardless of whether Europe's biggest shipper had moved me out here, in the end, it would still come down to mules for the last leg of the journey. There was no way around that unless you wanted to carry it all on your back. Trying to explain this to transport companies in England had been very frustrating. All their fancy slogans about shipping anything from anywhere to everywhere came crashing down when one tried to explain where I wanted the goods sent. So, I decided best to do it myself.

It was winter when my friend Simon and I set off. Unsurprisingly, he doesn't speak to me anymore, even the offer of a free holiday on Hydra hasn't tempted him to forgive the arduous journey we had. First, we had to battle the English Channel at night in winter on a large, rolling ferry, as I wanted to be in France at first light and cover a good distance down through Europe. We forgot to get our Swiss road tax sticker as we crossed from France through a remote border in the middle of the night into Switzerland. That oversight cost us later when we reached the border with Italy. My plan was to stop on the cusp of the Swiss and Italian Alps for the first night. How we made it that far in one day, I don't know, especially in an old white truck which had obviously logged quite a few miles on the clock. We pushed that white beast to its limit, crossing mile-high bridges and navigating excessively long Alpine tunnels, one after another, before emerging into the most amazing night sky in Courmayeur, a very popular Italian ski resort. However, it's not a place you want to be driving an old white truck through at night, in winter. We then dropped down to the Italian side of the Alps to Aosta. How lucky we were! Simon might not have agreed. It should have been zero degrees when we reached this point on that second day. It was hellish in the truck, and we were exhausted, the vehicle packed beyond common sense as we made the steep descent into the Aosta valley. As luck would have it, we hit the most unbelievable freakish weather, and it was 18°C that February. No snow or sleet, not even a drop of rain. Never thought I would welcome climate change, but it probably saved us. Still, we could not possibly go any further and stayed overnight in Aosta. We dined at a quaint little Italian trattoria, packed with disappointed skiers in their designer ski-gear, moaning about the lack of snow and us looking like a couple of very happy tramps.

The following day, we headed to Ancona for the overnight ferry to Patras in southern Greece. I decided that if I had to slum it in the white truck, I would at least live it up by booking two cabins on board the ferry for me and my then-friend. Just as well, as I collapsed by the time I got to the cabin, every muscle hurting, hungry but too tired to eat, just wanting to be able to stretch out horizontally for the first time in ages. But even that didn't go quite as planned. A crossing that should have taken seventeen hours ended up taking thirty.

I was deep in sleep when I felt the ship make a definite dip to one side, the port side for you seafarers. It was such a violent movement that it roused me from the depths of sleep, thoughts of *Titanic* went through my brain. But, as it turned out, nothing so sinister occurred, at least for us. Then came the announcement in several languages, "Due to a serious medical problem onboard, we will be returning to Ancona before resuming the voyage to Patras." It turned out a passenger had a suspected heart attack and needed to return to Ancona.

As we were already five hours out to sea, this meant it was going to take at least ten hours just to get back to the position we were in right now. I felt sorry for the sick person, but also for us onboard. I was pissed off, to say the least. Not very sympathetic, I know.

We finally arrived in Patras late the following night, too late to make it to Hydra for the evening. So instead, we opted for Nafplion. If you ever come to Greece, Nafplion is a must-visit. It is a most beautiful and elegant town, once the capital of modern Greece, and dominated by an almost complete Venetian castle known as the Palamidi. The waterfront is lined with a string of tavernas at one end and chic cafés at the other. Just behind the waterfront, I found the most charming town square that was so reminiscent of Italy.

However, as wonderful as Nafplion is I was in a hurry to get to Hydra. We were just about 30 kilometres from our journey's end, having travelled 1,500 kilometres, and I had to spend another night before I could get to Ermioni.

Ermioni is on the mainland opposite Hydra, where my now reluctant friend and driver, Simon, would be leaving me with my earthly possessions for the last sea transport to Hydra. I remember that day as I was euphoric. All I wanted was adventure! I just wanted this journey to never end. Would I really be able to get all my furniture and myself across from the mainland to my new island home?

The next morning, we set off early from Venetian Nafplion. I had been told that I should try get to Ermioni by midday to meet the Hydra cargo barge. It was a beautiful morning; clear striking blue skies that you only get in Greece. Warm in the sun, chilly in the shade. But it was the middle of winter after all.

Coming down the hill into the port of Ermioni, I wondered if the truck was going to make it those last few kilometres, and if that old cargo boat I remembered from my youth still operated. Then, sure enough, as we came into the port, there was the Aghios Georgiou steaming into the harbour.

How's that for timing, I thought. We had travelled 1,500 kilometres, been diverted, waylaid, delayed, and exhausted, only to then arrive at the same time exactly as the weekly cargo ship for Hydra.

My plan was then to unload everything on board this open-topped vessel, which had more rust than not, and wave goodbye to Simon. I could tell he was gagging to get as far away as possible by now. Then, I planned to ask the ship's captain if he would take me on board as well, even though passengers are not normally carried. I wanted to travel to Hydra for the last part of the journey together with my chattels and not wait until the passenger ferry in the morning.

This was when I first heard of the electricity strikes. They had been going on for a week, I was told. No one knew which area of Greece was going to be targeted by that flick of a switch to deprive them of power. That was the striker's strategy to cause as much chaos as possible. It works. Anyway, I had other issues to resolve; the sun was shining, and I could see "my" island just in the distance. So close, it was now getting really exciting. It took most of the day to get my beloved and now well-travelled possessions on board the Aghios Georgios. Luckily, Captain George had known Aunt Martha and allowed me to travel onboard. What a sight I must have made, perched there atop my furniture on the open deck, with the ship's bridge behind me, as we set off for the one-hour crossing to my new home. The light was fading, and as it grew darker, the lights of Hydra became more prominent. At least no electricity cuts here. Otherwise, there wouldn't be any twinkling lights in the distance. I felt like some macabre Cleopatra sitting on her throne whilst being carried from one dynastic empire to another. Well okay, I looked dishevelled and tatty, but with a little bit of imagination, who knows. I had on my old Paddington Bear type duffle coat, because even though it had been a lovely warm day, once the sun went down, the chills came out. Nor was I sat on a gilded throne, but on crates of general supplies, building materials, an ice cream fridge, my furniture, somebody's new furniture coming from IKEA in Athens according to the labels, and rusty old bits and bobs that obviously the captain thought important to keep this well-used cargo ship afloat.

Then, finally, I was there—Hydra Port—and what a view. It doesn't matter how many times I come into the harbour on Hydra, I am always dumbstruck by its beauty. It's almost amphitheatre shape is created by the charming houses that have not changed shape or colour on the outside at least for as long as anyone can remember. Building restrictions rule on Hydra, and no house can be more than three storeys and dominate the house behind it. No one can even change the colour of their shutters and doors legally. The waterfront is exactly what one expects and hopes to find. Packed tight, one long curvature of cafés, tavernas, tourist and upmarket shops, and plush banks with the obligatory marble fronts and interiors.

At this time of year, there isn't the plethora of the multi-million-dollar pleasure crafts and yachts that you get in the summer months. Still, there were a few obviously year-round sailors resting on their sailing boats and motor cruisers tied up in front of Banderas Café—no relation to Antonio, unfortunately. The Aghios Georgios had her special reserved spot between the luxury craft on one side and the small local fishing boats on the other, almost acting like a demarcation between new and old, rich and poor.

That was as far as the transportation went that night. No unloading in the dark. Mules don't work at night. I should be back at seven in the morning to claim my goods and have them transported the last few, but steep, steps.

As eager as I was to get up the hill to my new home, I thought it would be best to have something to eat down at the waterfront, buy a few basic supplies, and then head up. Hydra is one of only a few Greek islands that are properly open all year round. Not that every single shop, bar, and restaurant is open twenty-four seven, but many are. Zephyros Taverna was my first port of call. Firstly, because it was the choice of locals for winter fodder and, secondly, the lawyer had left the keys to Martha's House there for me to pick up.

I had just sat down to order my meal when *bang*!—the dreaded power cut. It was Hydra's turn to go without electricity for a few hours. Not to worry though, I was told; they cooked with gas and had more candles than the local monastery. It all looked quite charming, in the beginning at least. Typical blue checked tablecloths. The taverna quite full of Hydra locals and winter residents, the "year-rounders", candles on the table, Sofia and her husband cooking on the gas hob. Romantic, even. But how was I going to cope if this was to be part of my normal day-to-day life? If I got a power cut in London for five minutes, I would have been floored. Governments have fallen for less. Yet here I was, in a land where such disturbances are accepted as quite normal. The food was fine, not fancy but filling. I was obviously creating some interest from the locals. Who exactly was I? Was I really going to take over Martha's House and try and run it as a hotel? Where was I from? My appearance, looks, mannerisms, and surname, should they know it, would give me away and denounce me as "xeni"—a foreigner. Athenians are foreigners on Hydra. The relative of a long-time Hydra resident, Aunt Martha, was and still is definitely a foreigner.

I am sure my fellow patrons at Zephyros that night couldn't wait for me to leave so they could all discuss this at length. I didn't want to keep them guessing and from their beds for too long, nor me from mine. They needed me to go so they could openly tell the other what they knew, or thought they knew, about me. So, I paid the bill, was given a candle to find my way "home" and I set off up the hill in the complete darkness to find Martha's House. One local comedian shouted out "Kalo Pasca," Happy Easter! Unless you have experienced a Greek Orthodox Easter, then it would be a very curious remark. In explanation, at Easter in Greece, just about everyone goes to church in the evening on Easter Saturday, clutching a candle, waits till midnight, when all lights go out and the priest first lights his candle from a flame which has come all the way from the Church of the Holy Sepulchre in Jerusalem. The church in Jerusalem was built around the place where Jesus Christ is believed to have been crucified and buried. One by one, the flame is passed from person to person until everyone in and out of church has their candle lit by this holy of holy flames. Then all trundle off home in the darkness, clutching their candle to keep the flame alive. The challenge is to get your candle home without the flame going out, then draw a cross above your door entrance with the smoke to bless your house for the coming year. So next time you go to Greece, take a look above someone's doorway; I am sure you will see a cross made of black smoke. Now you know how and why it got there.

CHAPTER 12

As much as Aunt Martha loved the island and spent most of her later years here all year round, as far as I was concerned, a Greek island in winter is not the projected fantasy depiction of holiday posters. Certainly not on a windy February night, stumbling about in the dark trying to open the door from the cobbled street to Martha's House's inner courtyard, with only a candle to guide my way.

They say out of chaos comes order, like a phoenix rising from the ashes. Right then, at that moment, I felt I was a long way down in the depths of the ashes with a mouth full of dirt and very little chance of raising a finger, let alone rising through to some brilliance above. But life is made up of challenges, right? Trying to get that damn key in the lock of the blue-painted door, straining to a mix of nerves and excitement to see what lay waiting for me beyond.

It was a huge key, and I had a problem turning it as the place had obviously been shut up for some time. I entered into the charming white, stone-tiled terrace lined with shrubs and plants in pots I remembered from my youth, but now everything around me was crying out for some attention. Beyond the terrace, one could see another front door leading straight into Martha's House—well, one would have been able to see if there had been any electricity! This was the original house on the property, built about 200 years ago, and slightly modernised since. I was standing almost three-quarters of the way up what people refer to as "Hydra's Amphitheatre." Martha's House is built into the side of the hill, perched over the town and port with views across the Argo-Saronic Gulf to the mainland beyond. Apart from the renovations of nearby mansions and small villas by wealthy Athenians and foreigners who knew a good thing when they saw it, the view couldn't possibly have changed much in the 200 years since Martha's House was first built. I'm not sure what it was called then; it was most likely named after the family that had previously owned it.

To the right, there are steps leading to another terrace above, overlooking the courtyard where I was standing. Beyond the upper terrace, I could see a larger, typical white-painted building, also with blue shutters. Blue shutters are, as I'm sure you know, more than typical in Greece; they are "de rigueur." Up there was the "guest" part of Martha's House, and the building directly in front was where Aunt Martha had lived for the last half-century or so before her ill-fated journey "home."

I had this incredible urge to start investigating every single room, brick, plant, and panorama. I had memories of the place, of course; I could see there had been some significant changes. The house looked smaller than I remembered, and the lemon trees looked big, but not as huge as the bougainvillea which now completely dominated the building. It was virtually impossible to explore in the dark, and I was completely exhausted by my long journey from London. First things first, I needed shelter, a bed for night. I hoped that it would be possible to find a comfortable bed made up in the two-story building in front of me. Or, I would have to go up to the next level and forage amongst the guest rooms Aunt Martha used to rent out. I decided to head straight into what had been Aunt Martha's personal domain; to go further up, more stairs, in the dark with just a candle would be a bit silly.

As I stood there in the courtyard, not in the best of moods, I still couldn't help but be amazed at the views. Even in the early evening with no power across the island, other than candles flickering here and there, Venetian villas and typical two-story white Greek island houses dominated. It was antique silence and stillness in a modern-day, strike-ridden blackout. In the darkness, I could glimpse something of this living museum of a town, lit with an abundant supply of candles outlining a rich, velvet flat sea beyond the port.

Tearing myself partly away from the views, I managed to find the second gaggle of keys in the huge bunch I had been left at Zephyros Taverna. Finally, I broke through Martha's House's second line of defence and entered the dark, shuttered living room.

From the limited range of light from the candle I was holding, it didn't look too bad—much as I remembered it. The floor was tiled in the same white stone tiles as the courtyard. There was a reasonably large, country-style kitchen, with a few pots and pans dangling from butcher's hooks in the ceiling. There were two bamboo lounge chairs with some old cushions and the biggest TV I had seen outside of a Greek café, which I later learned was exactly where the television had come from. It was a gift to Aunt Martha from an old café-owning flame who decided to go "plasma" ready for the forthcoming European football championships. Aunt Martha had been kind enough, I suppose, to leave this oversized and outdated monolith of a television to me, along with a huge fridge and a few dusty but quite charming paintings of Hydra. For some reason, which I hadn't quite worked out yet but would become apparent, Aunt Martha didn't think taking these two large objects—television and fridge—plus the memories of Hydra in sketches, was worth the effort when she left the island. There was also the old biscuit tin that Aunt Martha had brought out with her from England in 1955, next to a silver framed faded photograph of Martha and some friends at the Acropolis in Athens. I remembered that tin; it was still where it always was, on the coffee table. I opened it up and, God bless her, it was full of candles.

There are two bedrooms off this large but tired-looking living space. One had two single beds and had been made up for me; obviously, someone cared a little, and I was grateful. Having placed the candle—my sole source of light and heat—in a strategic place, along with the biscuit tin of candles, I collapsed on one of the single beds.

I am not exactly sure what I was thinking right then, but I am pretty sure it was some disturbing thought. What on earth had my aunt got me into? Here I was, halfway up a Greek mountain, in the pitch dark on a small Greek island called Hydra, where, at that time, not a drop of water could be found other than rainwater, or what came in by a weekly petrol-fumed boat, making it totally undrinkable. No light, no hot water to shower, and tomorrow my personal possessions would be arriving. This was it. I couldn't just have a few weeks' holiday, move on, check into another hotel, let alone go back to where I came from. I had arrived, and now I had to stay and make a life here. Why on earth had Aunt Martha chosen this life, not just for herself but also for me? One plus point was that I spoke some Greek, learnt when I was working in Athens many years before, teaching English as a foreign language. Apart from the usual hello and goodbyes, I was not going to be able to communicate with the locals that much, less still if they decided to break into their local Hydriot dialect.

Suddenly, without my even realising it for a few moments, the power was back on! Oh my, how you appreciate something that's normally part of one's everyday life when it's taken away. I heard some rumbling, which was obviously the fridge kicking into gear, and I could see lights on in the other room. Amazing how tiredness can come and go so quickly. This was great; I could now have a hot shower, get a drink, switch on the giant telly, do some exploring and find out what's going on in my new little Martha's world. I could even go back out on the terrace without falling over something and have a good look around my Pandora's Box of a property. What I couldn't do is going back where I had come from or move on somewhere else.

Martha's House, my home! Still seems strange. So that's how more or less I arrived here that night and, after an eventful day, fell into a deep sleep, knowing that I would need all my strength the next day; this was only the beginning.

CHAPTER 13

The earth did shake for me that first morning. But it wasn't an earthquake. Light was just creeping in through the shutters and through the glass panels in the blue, wooden, hand-carved door directly in front of the bed. I had, in the end, chosen to crash in one of the guest rooms on the first night. Made me feel like I was just on holiday and this wasn't serious. Foolish, I know.

Slight movement of the bed. Then more clip-clops followed by voice grunting "brrrah…" This, I came to learn, was mule-speak. The mule drivers have one guttural sound for "go" and another for "stop." They all do it. It's quite strange really, but maybe compared to everything else around here, it's quite normal. No alarm clock needed. The mule men were on their way down to the port. The path took them past around Martha's House, then down Donkey Poo Lane. Now I knew how our street got its name. It was the main flight path for mules and donkeys. Down about six in the morning and back up around seven in the evening. No doubt, out there, going just past the other side of my bedroom wall, were my delivery beasts, going down to carry all that nonsensical stuff I had driven all the way from London, up the last few metres to Martha's House. Poor beasts. I really felt sorry for them.

They had no idea what waited for them down there at Hydra's port, spilling out of the Aghios Georgios. I reluctantly fell out of bed. I think after driving for four days to get here, I was now too tired to care about anything or where I was and just wanted to sleep. But there was work to be done. I had to get down to the port and coordinate the unloading. Also, I had about one hour to clean up Martha's House's dusty, cobweb-filled living space, to make room for my furniture. After all, how can you put your stamp on a place unless you add your own personal touches and knick-knacks? I probably didn't really need half of what I brought out from London, but it was all here now and I had to get it all sorted.

The scene down at the port was reminiscent of ancient waterfront times, albeit filled with more modern goods: chairs, tables, fridges, goods for the many mini-supermarkets of Hydra, building materials, air conditioning units—all the stuff that I had either sat on or been surrounded by when I had come over on the cargo boat the night before. Whatever Hydra's residents relied upon to build or repair their houses, to eat, to sell, to treasure were all contained in that shipment, now being dispersed on the very lively little port.

Squashed in between two of the cafés close to the boat's mooring, all of Hydra's weekly cargo was being taken off the boat and moved onto the quayside. The scene was one of mayhem, but somehow, it all seemed to work. Mules, donkeys, and mule men were in position surrounding this growing mountain of human valuables and eagerly awaited goods. Somewhere amongst all the cacophony of sound and crates were my precious goods, on the last leg of their journey to Martha's House where they could finally rest.

Now was the time for the owners of the goods to push and shove their way through the newly created alleyways of parcels and boxes and identify which ones were theirs. Pointing out to one's *mularis,* mule man, this box, that crate, perhaps tables and chairs haphazardly bubble-wrapped onto a pallet over there. Owners then retreat to the back, or even take their place at their preferred local café adjacent to this scene that has remained unchanged for centuries, whilst the *mularis* take over—lifting, moving, shoving, shouting at this and that, swearing absolutely compulsory—pulling out the goods they have been hired to deliver and moving them closer to their mules and donkeys to load up and send on their way up through the winding streets to wherever they needed to go.

Somehow, it all seemed to work and within a few hours, the whole ship had been unloaded, the goods collected and packed onto mules and donkeys. I seemed to have ten times more mules than anyone else, probably because I kept haggling with the mule guys about not overloading. I felt sorry for the poor beasts. For centuries on this island, they had been used to carry people and belongings up and down, but that was before fridges and giant sofas. Not that I had either. I decided there and then that there was no way I would be using any mularis and his mules who overloaded or didn't look after them like I would my animals.

The quay was then washed down, and the nearby café owners brought out more tables and chairs where the day's shipments had been, extending their café "footprint." Within minutes of the unloading being finished, the scene down at the port was now totally different. "Café Calm" had replaced "Cargo Chaos," almost as if the latter had never existed. All was as it should be again, and just in time too as very soon, yet another large ship, the *Aghios Demetrious* this time, would be making its way into Hydra harbour. Its precious cargo: day-tripper tourists from every continent of the world, on their three-islands, one-day cruise around the Saronic Gulf. From 100 to 300 tourists could come in, disembark, look, maybe but not always shop, get a mule ride round the town, maybe eat a little, and then get back on and be off to the next port all within two hours. A nuisance to some who like the tranquillity of Hydra, but for a few hours those day trippers provide a needy existence to all the little shops around the harbour and add life to a small island community.

I had to get back up the hill before the mules with my delivery arrived. Once I got back up there, I had cleaned up as best I could and sat in the winter sunshine waiting, not sure what I was waiting for, but I was waiting. I really had no idea how all my furniture was going to get up the 200 steps to Martha's House. I was in my own little world, taking in the stillness, birds darting in and out of the lemon trees on Martha's House's terrace, amazing views of Hydra town, the blue sparkling Mediterranean, and the outer ring of volcanic-shaped little islands beyond acting as guardians to the shores of the Peloponnese. Then, even further in the distance, majestic mountains with a sprinkling of snow at their peaks; this was still official winter after all. They say you know when spring has come, as the snow on the Peloponnese disappears overnight. Could I ever tire of this panorama? I think not. My daydreaming and view were then brutally broken by seeing just above the garden wall, my hand-carved Balinese chair floating past the wall, disappearing for a second behind the large blue outer door, then reappearing, just peeking above the garden wall at the other side.

I rushed over to the wall and looked down to the street, and there was this big mule, carrying the first of my boxes. Behind this mule, there were seven other smaller mules all tied head to tail, with my prized worldly possessions. Excitement at seeing my goods and chattels finally here at their new home, mixed with sympathy for Mr Mule and his mates! The mules of Hydra should be celebrated and worshipped. Replaced by the White Van elsewhere, these beasts of burden are not a drain on precious energy sources. Yes, their pollution is rather unpleasant, but not noxious. In fact, there were at that time EU subsidies for keeping them—for keeping donkeys actually, but mules are almost the same thing. No wonder Aunt Martha left her furniture behind. The logistics and cost of moving on Hydra are extremely challenging and for me very emotional when I see the donkeys, mules, and horses all lined up in the port.

The rest of the day unfolded similarly, with mules ascending the hill and unloading; at least, they only carried a few little boxes each. Then, just as the sun was going down, it was all done. Everything was delivered, and most things were more or less where they should be. Marvel of marvels, there was only one causality: a lampshade that had come off up the hill and ended up permanently as a hat for one of the mules.

I had brought out Aunt Martha's tables, chairs, and a nice comfy day bed onto the terrace. As soon as the last box had been delivered, my boisterous and excited mule drivers couldn't wait to be invited in. Taking it upon themselves to grace me with their company by plonking themselves down around the table, calling for a beer, an ouzo, or a little whisky, together with a little loukoumi—Greek for sweet, a very sugary delight similar, dare I say, to Turkish Delight. This was a local custom, and as much as I just wanted to tear open boxes and start getting everything sorted, I knew I had to partake in this tradition. They would not leave until they have conveyed good wishes for my house, my health, my arrival on the island, the upcoming season, my future children, and anything else they could think of until the bottle was drained and the sweets all consumed. Then off they all went, untying their mules in the street in front of the Martha's House and heading further up the hill to where the mules slept, and, if the beasts were lucky, to a stable and some land to run around in.

I had my chattels; everything was fitting where I imagined it should, and it all started to look a bit like home. Some imagination was needed, of course, but in Greece, that's not hard to come by.

CHAPTER 14

N ow that I had my furniture and bits and bobs, I had to focus on settling in and starting the task of running a guest house. That optimism was my first mistake—one of many, as it turned out. How could I be so naive to think that Greek bureaucracy couldn't possibly be that hard to wade through? I still can't believe how much I underestimated the rapacious, convoluted, conflicting, and borderline insane official processes one has to navigate to set up a business in some countries. I recall seeing programmes on British television about people who sell everything and, with little money or borrowed money, decide to move to a sunnier clime and start a business they have no prior experience in, where they don't speak a word of the local lingo. My heart goes out to them, especially those who survive and stay. I was lucky that, courtesy of Aunt Martha, I had Martha's House lock, stock, and cisterna below, where the rainwater was stored. Plus, I could sort of make my way in Greek. But nothing absolutely nothing could have prepared me for what lay ahead.

Firstly, you must register your property purchase with the local land registry. Lawyer Condos had already organised for the property to be passed to me on Aunt Martha's permanent departure as a sale, rather than inheritance. This, he said, would be the lesser of two evils, much easier than dealing with Greek inheritance laws, or something like that which I never quite understood. I was lucky that the land registry at that time was on the island. Finding it was an adventure in itself. "Next to the main church," I was told, "behind the port near Tasso's Café." I walked round the church, I walked in the church, I walked outside to Tasso's Café and asked again. After about thirty minutes, I eventually found the so-called land registry, the main archive and treasury of every single piece of property and proof of ownership on the island.

How could I have missed it, I wondered. By the side of the church was a small, steep marble staircase, with worn concave steps leading up to old monk cells that encircled the church on an upper level. The monks were long gone. Now, various local government officials occupied these cells. Their roles were mysterious; some collected the taxes for water supply, others for local sales tax. Some dealt with pensions and health care, and finally, there was one little cell where all the land sales and purchases over the years on the island were kept. Reminiscent of a hobbit house, even I, not exactly of Amazonian proportions, had to stoop to enter. The windowless cubbyhole was dark and claustrophobic, its walls laden with large black leather files stored on roughly made shelves, each numbered sequentially. One of these related to Martha's House and would have all the owners recorded from whenever these parchments of property had first started to be collected until the present day.

Inside the cell sat a young girl; she didn't look more than seventeen, but she must have been older to hold the illustrious position of local registrar. Melete introduced herself, named after one of the nine Muses. She had an intelligent-looking face, typical of the island, and with long shiny black hair tied back in a ponytail. I remember seeing and talking to her months later when I was walking over the hills across to another part of the island, as she rode past me on her white horse, going to place flowers on her grandfather's grave at the little cemetery in the hills to the south of Hydra port.

Back to the here and now. Was she the registrar? No, she was the registrar's clerk, but she had a telephone, and she could talk to the registrar who lived in Piraeus. The city of Piraeus is the main port for Athens and is two hours away by hydrofoil; this is where much of the governmental control of Hydra and neighbouring islands is managed. The best Melete could do was take my purchase documents and give me a receipt. She didn't have the authority to stamp the purchase documents and give me yet another document back to confirm that the property had been registered in my name.

This is something of great importance in Greece, as I was told by Mr Condos Junior. Apparently, until your property purchase is officially registered, the seller can sell it again to someone else, or worse still, someone could claim that they bought it. I knew it would be very unlikely that Aunt Matha's lawyer or anyone else would be party to such an outrageous act, but still, I wanted my precious stamped receipt of the registration as soon as possible. In any case, without it, I couldn't officially get electricity, television, telephone, and goodness knows what else in my name. However, nothing could be done as the registrar in Piraeus was on sick leave or was "working" from home. When she wasn't on sick leave, she only came out to the island once or twice a week, stamped what needed to be stamped, and returned the same day. What followed was two weeks of playing cat and mouse, waiting for the registrar to grace Hydra with a visit. By then, Melete had gotten to know me quite well, and I had her lined up to telephone me immediately when the registrar put in an appearance on Hydra. I was determined to be first there with my papers, thirsty for that all-important official stamp. Stamps are very important in Greece. In fact, many people have one with their name and tax number on it and maybe their official position if they have one, that is. Some have more than one stamp, and it's not unusual to see those circular stamp holders on desks with six or more stamps, gaily being whisked around on their little carousel being slapped down on one document or another, overlooked for the stamp hanging next to them for another document and sometimes never used at all. Even I have a stamp now. I hate to admit, I actually have two, and a third stamp is on its way to me, according to my accountant. It's amazing what power it gives you as you reach for your stamp and bang it down on some bit of paper, maybe adding more authority to the document by scribbling your signature as well.

Eventually, the registrar and I met, and her precious stamp, plus signature, were added to my precious property purchase document. I was so happy that day, feeling I had achieved so much that, before running back up to Martha's House, I dropped into Dora's sweet shop in the main square behind the church and bought a box full of small pastries, which I popped back to the monk's cell as gifts for the girls who worked there.

This proved to be the easy part. What then ensued were nearly two months of running back and forth between Piraeus, Athens, Poros, and back to Hydra. There must have been more than a dozen different government departments involved in setting up Martha's House as a business and registering for tax. When I see those little old ladies all dressed in black, waiting by the port for the ferry boats of tourists to arrive, offering rooms to rent for a night, I often wonder if they too had gone through the same tortuous process I did, to ensure everything was legal. I doubt it. That was in the old days before Airbnb and Booking.com. I wasn't all dressed in black, yet, and hanging around the port with a "room to rent" sign seemed to have been replaced by locals sidling up to tourists and asking them if they needed a room. My mission was to do this legally and properly. More fool me.

CHAPTER 15

Once the land registry was finally settled, I set about planning to give Martha's House a facelift. The once-white walls needed painting, and the guest rooms lacked air conditioning, curtains and even shower curtains. Worse, there were no emergency cords in the bathrooms. Here in Greece, they are mandatory in guest rooms. I ordered a dozen and had them installed. They weren't connected to anything except a red light in the bathroom, but they satisfied the authorities. Hopefully, no one would ever need to pull the cords, as there was no ambulance service on the island. My fallback plan was to call one of the mule men to transport the potential casualty to the local hospital, which merely acted as a triage centre.

The list of mandatory requirements for guest rooms and hotels was endless. A friend of a friend who worked at the Greek organisation of tourism sent me a rough list of what I needed to do to receive an official license to operate. There was no official list, just ever-changing criteria altered at an inspector's whim. Due to the months spent getting to this point, I had only a few weeks left to start marketing Martha's House and taking bookings. I was fast running out of savings. I had to be ruthless with priorities and find some workers as it was the beginning of April and Greek Easter was upon us. The first possible worker contact on the list was a fellow who had been Aunt Martha's handy man of sorts.

Aunt Martha had highly recommended Dikos the Albanian. He had changed her light bulbs, maintained the garden, fixed leaking water tanks, and mended broken windows. Dikos came with excellent references. There's a pecking order on the island, varying depending on who you ask. To a Hydriot, locals come first—that is, bone fide Hydriots born and who went to school on the island—followed by wealthy Athenians, then expats who own local houses, and long-term expats who rent. Albanians, Bulgarians, Ukrainians, and Georgians came last. Expats, however, might put themselves first and locals second. More fool them. Anyone who has spent any period in Greece knows that Albanians provide most of the local hard labour and work force. Most Greeks would also argue that they also provide most of the crime. That wasn't my general experience. When I first came to Hydra, there was virtually no crime; anyone attempting it, Albanian or otherwise, would likely be expelled by the local chief of police in two shakes of a bottle of retsina.

Dikos, an Albanian resident of over a decade, seemed to possess some sort of human radar; he always knew when I returned to the island from one my futile visits to a government department on the mainland, appearing on my doorstep within ten minutes of my arrival.

I started with Dikos but didn't finish the job with him. While he was punctual and hardworking, his bill of five thousand euros for two weeks of work was unreasonable. I knew that he would normally make about ten to fifteen euros an hour; to say that he had done 400, if not 500 hours' work, in two weeks was just a stretch too far, especially coupled with him retiling my bedroom floor with mismatched tiles.

Dikos was fired, but he returned a few days later asking for an additional one thousand euros as an advance for future work. When refused, he returned a third time and told me a sob story about his ten-year-old son accidentally burning his house down in Albania, implying the rebuild should be at my expense. If Aunt Martha had surrounded herself with the likes of Dikos, it's no wonder her wealth had depleted while theirs had increased.

After a few enquiries around town, I found a replacement. "Penko is your man," I was told. "He's Bulgarian, *but* you can trust him. He's not like the rest." I wasn't sure what was meant by "he's not like the rest." Penko, which apparently means stone or rock in Bulgarian, seemed a fitting name for a builder. At our first meeting, I outlined my vision for Martha's House, emphasising the tight schedule. Despite our accented Greek, he understood, evaluated the job independently, and quoted a price. We shook hands on the deal. Penko and his team were punctual, meticulous, and billed exactly as agreed, without any fuss or quibbles. The only irksome incident involved the customary long lunch, traditionally cooked by the maid or housekeeper, during which Penko expected me to join them for a daily feast at my expense and share wine. Not my idea of a lunch break. I let it happen a few times in the beginning, but then put a stop to it. I didn't want to spend two hours every day having lunch and then wait around till ten o'clock at night for them to catch up and finish for the day. Instead, I promised a slap-up meal for all at a good taverna when it was all done.

Dikos was most put out when he heard that a Bulgarian had replaced him. I was told there was a bit of a spat down in the port one night when Penko and Dikos came face to face. Dikos backed off in the end, not because Penko had the body of a wrestler, but because Penko also ran the cinema on Hydra, which was a major form of entertainment in the summer months and Dikos didn't want to be banned from the red carpet of the Hydra Regal show time. Nothing more was heard about it all and Dikos has never come by again. I hope he has managed to rebuild his house and discipline his son.

CHAPTER 16

The most harrowing part of the official paper chase was arguably the visit to Poros to see the local tax office. Greek bureaucracy is a maze of confusion, with various departments scattered across neighbouring islands, Piraeus, and Athens. During that time, dealing with the tax office, located on the island of Poros, was particularly daunting. Poros, a charming island town popular among tourists and yachting enthusiasts, is greener and busier than Hydra but each island has its unique allure.

Lurking beneath this beauty and touristic fun was the εφορία – eforia - the tax office, a place as scary to most Greeks as the Stasi were to East Germans. Housed in a quaint eighteenth century renovated neoclassical building, overlooking Poros port made it even more dangerous as the loveliness of the offices, from the outside at least, disguised a house of potential horror within. I was warned how tricky this department could be to deal with, so for my visit I went armed with my accountant's dogsbody, the all-around very confident Melina. Nothing to worry about, Melina said, she had a contact there and he would guide us through everything. I just had to make sure that I had my land registry papers, courtesy of Melete at the monk's cells, and the license I had obtained a few days earlier from the Ministry of Tourism following their inspection to show that I had met the criteria to open as a guest house. Contrary to Melina's confidence, mine completely dissolved when I saw "our man" come out from behind his caged teller's desk wearing a T-shirt with the words in English that read, "I don't give a fuck." Since Mr Takis the taxman didn't really speak English, I wondered if he actually knew what his T-shirt read. I was probably the only native English-speaking person in the place at the time. No one else took the slightest bit of notice. Was I the only soul who found it quite strange and unnerving that a government employee, on duty, in the tax office who was in fact a tax inspector, would walk around brandishing attire that shouted, "I don't give a fuck"?

Mr Takis was busy, curt but not unpleasant. However, he said that before he could give me the most important tax number so I could start operating, he would have to come to Hydra and inspect Martha's House. A bit of a wasted trip to Poros, I thought, surely this could have been done on a phone call. Sometime the following week the inspection would take place. Melina said not to worry, he probably won't come up the hill, anyway, and if he does, he will just say he saw it and that would be it.

After waiting four days for Mr Takis to turn up, he managed to call on the fifth day when I was out walking the island to get a breather from it all. Luckily, I had my mobile on, so Penko, who stayed behind to do some running repairs, was able to call me when a puffing, red-faced, and not-too-happy-to-be-there Mr Takis the Tax Man turned up at four in the afternoon on a Friday.

I was having a lovely time at Vlychos. About a thirty-minute walk round the coast road from Hydra town. Vlychos boasts a few houses, two tavernas, and a beach with umbrellas and sun loungers. Just past this first beach is my little hide away—a jewel in Hydra's crown, complete with a little jetty with clear turquoise water. I could lie for hours on that jetty just taking in the tranquillity and beauty of it all. My bliss was broken by the call and Mr Takis came on the line, telling me that he was at Martha's House and how nice she looked and asking when did I buy all those furnishings and so on. Pretty innocent questions. He simply asked me to come back to Poros the following Monday with all the receipts of what I had spent on Martha's House in the last few months to finalise the matter.

Good news, I could soon get that tax number now and start operating.

The following Monday morning saw me catching the first early departure on the Hydrofoil from Hydra to Poros. The Hydrofoil usually starts off at six in the morning from Porto Heli, stops at Spetses, then Hydra, onto Poros, before unloading its final passengers at Piraeus by 9 am. It's quite a busy departure, with people going to Athens for a day's business, bureaucracy, or shopping. Others at the end of their holidays and returning to Athens for the flight home.

I insisted Melina come with me again, my Greek just wasn't good enough to talk tax-speak. We had just a short sea journey, forty minutes to Poros, then disembarked with all the other hopefuls and accountants going to the "eforia." The walk from the drop-off point to the tax office was very pleasant, leading along a vibrant waterfront, with cafés starting to fill up, tavernas, fishermen who at that time of the morning were mending their nets after a night's fishing, and various yachts and motorboats tied up at the quay side. It was spring now and even at eight in the morning you could start to feel the power of the sun. Contrastingly, the tax office was again icy cold, feeling and smelling like a morgue behind that wonderful neoclassical facade. The air conditioning was up full blast, even though it wasn't that hot yet outside. They were preparing. The staff at the tax office seemed more disciplined than most government offices, arriving at opening time to prevent the formation of lengthy queues of stressed, panic-ridden citizens clutching reams of papers, all in pursuit of the crucial "stamp" of some official.

There was no queue yet, so I was able to go straight in just as Mr Takis arrived. "Have you got the receipts?" he asked. Yes, of course, and he took the file of my carefully sorted receipts for Martha's House's new trimmings. "You should be done in no more than thirty minutes," he said. Taking the word 'done' as a positive thing, I thought wow, I couldn't believe it; this was going so well. I would be in and out within thirty minutes. Melina and I could then go and have a latte and a pastry in one of those lovely little cafés before catching the 11am departure back to Hydra. I felt good. Despite what everyone told me, I was sure now that Greece wasn't such a bad place to do business and as long as you stuck to the right path, all would be fine. I found it ridiculous that so many people everywhere prefer to live in a "black economy" and try to dodge any kind of legal process. If you don't pay your taxes, how can there be roads, mule tracks for us on Hydra, schools, police, and tax offices?

I sat and waited. Thirty minutes came and went. The tax office started to fill up. An argument, one of many, broke out between a young man and another tax inspector behind the cage. I couldn't help eavesdropping. From what I could understand, with Melina's whispering assistance, the young man had inherited a house some years ago from his grandfather, renovated it, and had been operating as rooms to let. He had come in to pay his tax on earnings, declaring his revenue for the past year. But the payment was being refused by the tax collector. It was strange, I thought. Why would a tax man refuse to collect taxes? My ears were now straining to hear the conversation, if you can call it that, as this was quite a similar situation to mine. "All your renovations are illegal," he was told, "and I don't care if you got planning permission; that's nothing to do with tax. You should have informed us before you had started the renovations so we could inspect the property beforehand."

Well, well, well. This was another rung in the ladder of bureaucracy that I had never heard of. I was so glad I had all my receipts, all carefully hole-punched, stapled, and filed.

As it neared ten-thirty, Melina got very restless; she had to return to Hydra on the next ferry no matter what. I was concerned about her leaving me; it felt like being thrown into a gladiator ring. After she barged into the Directors office, she informed me that the Director of the Tax Office spoke English and would explain anything unclear to me. So, off went Melina, seemingly eager to leave.

An hour later, I grew concerned. Mr Takis avoided my gaze each time he darted to and from his cage, avoiding those who were queuing for their second stamp after managing to get the first one. When he couldn't avoid me any longer, he communicated through hand signals that it wouldn't be much longer.

Four hours later, having missed breakfast and lunch, I was told to see the Director. While waiting outside her office, held back by a crowd of other hopefuls all shouting something or another, I decided to go with the flow and introduced myself when I managed to barge in. Everyone was told to leave the room, but the door remained propped open, allowing a dozen people to linger and eavesdrop. Everyone left except a young girl, who seemed to be the Director's relative, sitting on a cluttered old sofa and playing with her mobile, looking bored.

"You realise you could face a very large fine and even prison," Director Anopouli informed me. I was completely floored! What on earth was going on here? On her desk was my precious file of receipts. A tirade then started during which my file was waved up and down, thrown back on the desk, opened, read from, thrown down again. How on earth could I have put myself in this situation? After about half an hour of the "interview," I was thinking okay let's

71

get this over and done with then, put me in jail and let me serve my time in peace, as anything is better than this.

My crime? Apparently, according to Greek Tax Code No E1234567-8 or whatever, I was required to wait until I had my tax number BEFORE making any changes or disposing of any furnishings and fittings. My crime probably was denying the Tax Office the opportunity to inspect such goods for disposal, to ensure they weren't being sold for profit, and to verify that the whole refurbishment wasn't a ruse.

I stood there stunned for what seemed like ages. Then, when there was finally a lull, I endeavoured to point out that firstly, I couldn't apply for the tax number until I also had a license from the tourist office. The tourist office wouldn't give me a license unless the property met their minimum criteria, necessitating the refurbishments. Further, I had in the file of receipts, confirmation from the local municipality of Hydra for the rubbish collection by mule and disposal of the goods in "dispute" so there is no way I could have sold them and surreptitiously pocketed the few euros I might have supposedly made. Moreover, I had "bought" a building and nowhere in the contract had I bought any furniture from Aunt Martha. Whatever remnants she left behind, I was surely entitled to dispose of without gracious inspection by the tax officers of Poros. Mrs Anopouli now pretended not to understand English and disregarded my explanation as rubbish.

It was a controversy-laden minefield. It was nearing four o'clock, the tax office closing time, and the last departure back to Hydra was at four-thirty. If I missed it, I would be stranded overnight on Poros, or worse, jailed.

Mr Takis was summoned again. He had set me up, having instructed me to bring those receipts so he could report me for spending money before official permission was granted. He refused to approve my tax number application. Eventually, Mrs Anopouli and I reached a compromise: no jail this time but I would have to pay a fine. Whilst all this was going on, people were coming and going in and out of that office, stamps were being bashed against documents, except mine, petty arguments, others told to leave and come back with an accountant. This was definitely not for the faint-hearted.

With about fifteen minutes left to catch my hydrofoil back to Hydra. Not much time to go back to the tax cage, get another tax inspector, not Mr Takis who now openly ignored me and was obviously upset that I hadn't been carried off by the local police. Another fee was then required, I was sent up to the first floor for that, got there. No, they can't accept the fee until the papers had been co-signed by the officer next to the director's office. You're not told that, of course, before you climb the stairs and queue. I rush back down get the co-director's signature, back up the first floor, more scrutiny, then the wonderful sound of stamp hitting paper as the fee is finally accepted. Not over yet, back down for another stamp from another tax employee of some unknown rank, but not before this new player in this farce checked that the man sitting opposite him had also signed off on the document and that the fee had been paid upstairs.

Finally, back out in daylight! How can it be so beautiful out here, I thought. The sun, blue skies, little boats, and tourists passing by, with locals sipping their third or fourth coffee of the day. And in there the "eforia," absolute hell on earth.

Reaching Hydra at the end of the day was total relief. I had phoned Susan, a new-found friend and expat married to a Greek and living on the island for decades, who came down to the port to meet me. I sat in one of the nearby cafés and sipped a coffee while I vented. One thing was for sure, Mr Takis lied on his T-shirt; Takis very much did give a fuck. He seemed intent on causing as much damage as possible, which requires significant determination and perseverance. Why he and, I hate to say it, some others I encountered on my journey to opening a guest house, acted this way still amazes me. Was it jealousy? Who knows, and I didn't care to find out now that I had my duly "stamped" papers and was recounting the whole nasty episode to Susan.

I believed I was now free to open Martha's House to paying guests, just in time for Greek Easter and upcoming bookings for the third weekend in June, when one of the biggest celebrations of Hydra was nearly upon us. The Miaoulis Festival.

CHAPTER 17

Admiral Miaoulis, a favourite son of Hydra from the time of the Ottoman Empire, joined the fight against the oppressors of Greece, playing instrumental roles in many major sea battles. His death on the 24th of June 1835 is commemorated with grand celebrations on Hydra. Visitors, mostly Greeks, partake in the three-day festivities of music, dance, and food, culminating with a re-enactment of a sea battle and an impressive fireworks display. By June, it's early summer, and the island bustles with activity. Tavernas and bars busy, seas now warming, and beaches full. During Miaoulia, every single room on the island is let and all those with holiday homes are usually in residence for this Greek televised event.

Martha's House, freshly painted and fully booked, shone in anticipation of appreciating guests. The garden was manicured, more plants were added, and tiles both inside and outside were scrubbed and gleaming. I waited eagerly, having spent a substantial amount of my savings due to legal processes, opening many months later than planned.

Most of my guests for Miaoulia were coming from Athens, apart from two rooms booked by Scandinavians—chalk and cheese guests, to say the least. The first to arrive that Friday night were a couple from the exclusive northern suburb of Athens, Kifissia.

They threw open the front gate and tumbled in, gasping for breath; they couldn't believe they had just climbed 200 steps. They couldn't even speak! I rushed forward with glasses of cold water. You would have thought they had crossed the Sahara in lead boots. "When you said it was high and over 200 steps, I thought you were joking," the woman told me. They were almost in shock; there were no cars or even scooters on the island—no transport whatsoever, other than donkeys, mules, and your own two feet. "What sort of place is this?" they said, a question that initially took me aback. After all, these were Greeks—surely, they knew that Hydra was famous for being car-free and built on the side of a 964-metre-high mountain. I was only about halfway up the Hydra hill; I can't imagine what they would have thought if Martha's House had been up further on the outer perimeter of Hydra Town. As more Athenians came and went, I realised that out of all the nationalities I welcomed to Martha's House, they were some of the least prepared for the island. By contrast, our Norwegian guests for that first weekend practically ran up the hill and didn't seem at all phased by my location. Instead, they were soaking in all the views, tranquillity, and coolness of the garden, and asking me if I knew Leonard Cohen. A regular question I came across, and no, I never met Mr Cohen. I think the last time he came to the island must have been in the 1980s. More on Leonard Cohen later as no story about Hydra can exclude the impact he had and still has on the island.

The initial experience with guests was akin to getting through a first night's stage performance—a sense of relief when it was over and a feeling of accomplishment when the guests were happy. After the Miaoulia weekend, I reflected on what had gone well and where I needed to improve. The 200 steps up a steep climb was proving difficult for all except those of Viking descent. I certainly needed a good reliable mule man and trusty well-looked-after mules on hand to assist guests with their baggage from the port. It only took a few calls to find Andreas. I had seen him around going back and forth to the port, mostly with building supplies. He wasn't one of the gang who hung around the port every day waiting for the tourist boats to come in, trying to sell rides round the town for a few euros. He was of a different class. I discovered that there are three distinct categories of mule and mule men you see. First there are those mules that just take tourists for quick rides round the town or maybe to Profitias Elias, the monastery at the highest peak above Hydra. Then there are those that carry suitcases, shopping, and locals up and down the hill. Lastly, there are the tough mules who carry furniture and building supplies. After all, you can't load a television on the back of a mule that's only used to carrying a tourist. Nor can you put a person on the back of a mule that has never had any human on its back – it would just freak out.

Andreas had two kinds of mules. One type for luggage and supplies and other for people. Andreas could meet Martha's House needs. He could bring up my weekly supplies from the supermarket, collect luggage to and from the port for guests, and provide a taxi service for those guests who didn't want or couldn't walk very far. The deal was done and best of all, I found out that Andreas was quite a serious young man with a family. He wasn't one of the *mularis* gang that spent half the day drinking ouzo or beer, nor did he expect me to provide him with a drink and loukoumi every time he dropped something or someone off at Martha's House. He looked after his animals, turned up when he was supposed to, did his job, and went home.

CHAPTER 18

It didn't take long for news to circulate round town that I had done a seasonal deal with Andreas. That meant that none of the others would get a look in, and those *mularis* who had been part of the group I used when I first came to carry my boxes up were quite put out. About two days after Andreas's appointment, I stepped out onto the terrace to find Costa and Manos, cousins who had carried up my goods and chattels back in February. They wanted to know why I had overlooked them in my choice of *mulari*, mule man. It was simple, really. They were too expensive, unreliable, and too cheeky for my liking, their cheekiness made obvious by their presence on my terrace, challenging my freedom of choice.

The conversation started out as civilised as it could be. However, everything I said had to be repeated by Costa to Manos at an almost screaming pitch. All this in Greek, which to the non-native speaker always sounds like people arguing and shouting anyway. I decided the only way to manage the situation was to act crazier than they did. I then put on my best crazy mad woman persona. They quickly left, cap in hand, saying no bad intent was meant; they just wanted to know what they had done wrong. Apologies all around and they were seen off.

In actual fact, Costa wasn't shouting at me at all. He was shouting at Manos because Manos was nearly totally deaf. Manos didn't have to endure deafness. The story, as it goes—and there is always a story about something on the island—is that one of Manos's girlfriends had a son who was jealous of the attention his mother was giving to Manos. One night when Manos was half asleep in front of the telly, the boy crept up behind Manos and banged his hands over Manos's ears with such force that it burst his eardrums. A local doctor had examined Manos and told him that an operation in Athens would mostly likely restore his hearing. However, Manos had never been off the island, nor did he want to. A life of silence was to him preferable than a sea trip and a hospital stay on the mainland.

The cousins weren't the only ones to object to our choice of Andreas. A few days later, I received a call from Mrs Stamata who lived close by and was also a *mularis,* as were her husband and her son when they were at home. The only female mule driver I had come across. I had bumped into her one day when I was down at the port. An educated woman, who spoke a number of languages, she believed she was a few classes above the other mule owners who, according to her, mostly had probably never even progressed past primary school. Mrs Stamata tried to convince me that dealing exclusively with her would be best as she could speak English, French, and some Italian. Plus, over the years, she had come to know most of the regular visitors to the island. She had a proposal. As she expected a premium for her taxi services, she would charge our clients the same as Andreas and then I could pay her another five euros per mule directly, and no one would be wiser, a deal between her and me. I couldn't figure out how this worked out as a good deal for me. I told her I found her proposal quite confusing. Pretending to be stupid, I discovered, was sometimes better than trying to appear smarter.

I assume upon hearing that Andreas was definitely our man now, Mrs Stamata eventually gave up on me accepting her ludicrous offer. She phoned me, cursing, to say as much, insisting I should never call her for help as she simply wouldn't be available. So what? Did I care? Not in the slightest. A few days later, I was relating this tale to a new "friend" I had discovered on the island, Aphrodite, originally from Hydra, who still kept a house here but now lived mostly in Athens after spending several years in Paris. "Don't take any notice of her, Zoe," Aphrodite advised. "She's mad, just like her whole family. Haven't you noticed how alike she and her husband are?" It turned out that Mr and Mrs Stamata were closer in family ties than is healthy. I never really found out how close, but it was significant enough that you couldn't tell her, her husband, or her son apart. The only distinctive, defining difference were the hands. The son had six fingers on one hand. Handy for knitting or tying knots, I suppose, but a little off-putting. The whole family was terribly shy, apart from Mrs Stamata, the obvious matriarch of the clan. Every time I saw them or passed them on my way down or up from the port, the husband and son looked up or away, anywhere but at me.

According to Aphrodite, deformities were commonplace on Greek islands. The island, in the past, had suffered the same fate as many isolated communities, with cousins marrying cousins repeatedly. In fact, she said her friend, a nurse at the local hospital, believed that about twenty-five percent of the local population had some sort of less-than-perfect bodily feature. Not that I consider myself to have the perfect body or face. However, I had never met anyone with six fingers before. I was initially sceptical of Aphrodite's claims, as I soon learned she was quite volatile and prone to exaggeration. On the other hand, I was finding it tough climbing all those Hydra steps to Martha's House, lugging the daily bread and pastries. I certainly couldn't do it as quick as my housekeeper Katerina and often trailed well behind some local octogenarian carrying twice my load. Hydra must be in one of those so called 'blue zones' where people live forever. They can't all be inbred I thought. The next day, I had to go to the post office. It was a really hot day even for the end of June, reaching almost 40C. On the way down, I was a little overcome by the heat, having spent most of the morning rushing around. I sat down on a little kerb by the side of the street, just staring down at the cobbles when these feet went past. A local woman's bow-shaped, muscular legs and open-toed sandals came into my line of vision. There, on her right foot, between her large toe and her second toe, was a "sixth" toe sticking straight up! Oh, my goodness, where would this end? Was the whole place full of mutants? I wouldn't have looked at anyone's hands or feet if Aphrodite hadn't brought the subject up. Now I couldn't help it, darting glances to the left and right as I went around town. Who else belonged to the "sixth" tribe of Hydra? I didn't really want to be doing this and I had to force myself to stop. Since that day, I haven't seen another "sixth" around the place. So maybe I just imagined it all....

CHAPTER 19

I had now established my daily routine. Each morning, I would rise and prepare breakfast for the guests. To be honest, my helper-cum housekeeper Katerina, also Albanian, did most of the work, setting up the buffet breakfast under the large umbrella in the cool part of the garden. She would lay out local yoghurt, honey, walnuts, cake, seasonal fruits such as watermelon, apples, grapes, little Greek *tyropitakia*—cheese pies—and freshly squeezed orange juice. Katerina and I would take turns going down to the bakery at seven in the morning to pick up freshly baked bread and delicious little creamed donuts that not even Krispy Crème could match.

One such morning, I heard a commotion by the waterfront followed by a huge splash, like someone had made a belly flop into the port. There weren't many people around as most Greeks, when on holiday, don't stir before ten in the morning. Just the locals who had some job to do and fishermen bringing in their night catches. To fit in with the locals, where standing around staring and gossiping is compulsory, I didn't hesitate to cross over to the port side to see what was happening. A man was being hauled out of the harbour, drenched, in what must have been a very nice light grey suit and shiny shoes, now dripping seawater. The debate was whether he fell or was pushed. One old man was adamant that this wasn't the first time and wouldn't be the last that someone had been pushed. A "*Malaka*" of the first order. An interesting word, "*malaka*." Its literal translation would be wanker or tosser, I suppose. It was considered a very naughty word when I first visited Greece in my youth, rarely heard. But returning now in my middle years, times had changed, and it seemed every other word, mostly by young men from eight years upwards, was "*malaka*." It was even now being used as a term of endearment. Like, "Hey, Malaka, how are you?" or "Haven't seen you in ages, Malaka." For sure, no one around me at this time was using the word "*malaka*" as a term of endearment for this expensively dressed man now sitting on the port, coughing up half the contents of Hydra's harbour. I didn't know what he had done, but he had obviously upset quite a few people. The owner of Nico's Bar came rushing over, seeming to be a friend of the wet man. Helping him to his feet, he was then escorted in the direction of the police station and possibly the hospital. "Serves him right, the 'malaka,'" one person said. "Should have held his head under for a good five minutes," said another. "Not at all," a voice at the back shouted. "Mr Elefteris is a good man and everything he does is for the benefit of Hydra." We, apparently, were the "malakas," not Elefteris, for not appreciating him.

By the time I reached the bakery a good sixty seconds later, the baker and his wife knew the whole story of what had happened at the other end of the port. I had to ask who Mr Elefteris was. "Miss Zoe, you don't want to know," I was told. "If you come to his attention, you better get your wallet out as you will be needing it to get you out of the trouble he will cause." All very mysterious. I had to get to the bottom of this, but the bread and donuts needed to be delivered first. I had guests waiting.

At the first opportunity, as casually as possible, I "bumped" into my local oracle, Aphrodite. I just knew she would know who Mr Elefteris, loosely translated as "freedom" in English, was. I wasn't disappointed. As I went past Aphrodite's house, her door was open and she called me into her kitchen where she was making some

Greek coffee. I asked if she had heard what had happened down on the port that morning. Of course, she had. "The whole of Hydra was talking about it and the man deserved it as well," not that she would tell him that to his face. "Revenge is one of his greatest pastimes. Whoever had the courage to 'accidentally' knock him into the harbour should be given a medal," that was a bit strong, I thought, coming from Aphrodite. "He had just pushed some people too far with his superiority and money-grabbing ways," there was no stopping Aphrodite now, she had to tell me more; one coffee wasn't going to be enough.

Mr Elefteris's story was an interesting one, aren't they all? Now in his mid-sixties, he had come to the island in the 1970s with his father, during the dark Greek Junta years. His father, a pro-Junta civil servant, had been appointed as Administrator of the Argo Saronic islands, of which Hydra was one such island. A position abolished once the Junta were subsequently overthrown.

These military despots were also in a position to ensure that their sons did not have to endure two years compulsory military service, in some remote spot on a Greek border, digging then filling in useless holes all day, or sitting around smoking or being shouted at and abused by superiors. These golden sons of the Junta could find a way out if they wanted. Their fathers simply gave them two-year assignments doing some obscure job on a nice island. His father became quite wealthy during that dark period; how, no one dares to say exactly, but rumour has it that it had something to do with the issuance, or not, as the case maybe, of building permits and government contracts. Freedom Junior, then the younger Elefteris, fell in love with Hydra in more ways than one and unluckily for the locals, and later expats with money, he stayed on after the Junta were thrown out and his father left. Elefteris had lived in the shadow of his father for many years. For him, it was a relief in a way when the days of the Junta were over. His father disappeared back to Athens as fast as he could, the role of island administrator scrapped.

Elefteris was left alone to be himself, which was unfortunate for the islanders as Elefteris had a huge bone of contention against most of them. Before Daddy had left, and when Elefteris was just twenty, he had fallen in lust. The recipient of his affections was none other than a locally based artist by the name of Demis. Demis didn't care if his sexuality was known or not. He was an artist and of the strong opinion he could do whatever and the more outrageous the better. Demis wanted Elefteris to move in with him and to hell if anyone on the island dared to comment. Conversely, Elefteris was absolutely not going to announce his love of Demis to anyone, let alone the island. In fact, Elefteris was already being lined up to marry a nice Greek girl from Athens with a big dowry. It all came to a head, so to speak, one night, when there was a huge argument between the two lovers. Demis was heard to say, "I am gay, you are gay, Elefteris, so why can't you just admit it and to hell with your Junta-sucking father." Elefteris's response was quite shocking; he spat back, "I am not gay, you are the gay one, Demis—I fuck *you*, you don't fuck me." And that, according to Aphrodite, was basically the end of the relationship, and she should know, as Demis was her first cousin. But the revenge was only about to start.

Demis decided to have an art exhibition in the Melina Mercouri hall, as its now known. For quite some time, Demis had been making secret paintings of Elefteris. What he had not painted of his former lover, he decided to make some minor changes to other paintings, showing nothing other than a series of his work depicting none other than Elefteris in various forms of adulation. From Elefteris butt-naked leaning out of a window, to Elefteris captured as a centaur with wings, hovering in the sky above a surreal Hydra, to Elefteris the matador with tunic, cut to his groin. The centrepiece, a tryptic of Elefteris the Merman, surrounded by highly sexualised-looking Mermen. The evening was apparently very well attended and not just for the free drinks and snacks. Most of the locals hated Elefteris's father and Elefteris himself for what they represented, the worst of the Greek Junta years, so to see this display of almost pornographic homosexuality depicting Elefteris was manna from heaven for them. It was a great success for Demis, not sure how many pieces of art he sold, though. Unfortunately, Demis wasn't there to personally witness his revenge. By the time the doors were flung open to the gallery opening, he was boarding a ferry at Patras bound for Bari in Italy. It was either that or Elefteris's father would have had Demis locked up on some trumped-up tax evasion charge or something. Apparently, Demis ended up in Paris claiming political asylum, insisting the Greek Junta was pursuing him for his democratic and liberal views. This, of course, was before Greece joined the European Union, so to get to France from Greece was no mean feat. In Paris, he became a leading art critic and lecturer of modern art. During my first year on Hydra, I was fortunate to spend an evening at one of his exhibitions. Returning now as the expatriate hero, Demis put on another show of his most recent work. From what I saw, nothing had changed really in thirty-plus years, except there were now long, thin, blonde matadors and nubile young men leaning out of windows. Not chubby dark-haired past lovers like Elefteris.

Nonetheless, Elefteris survived the humiliation, but had not forgotten. He had done very well for himself on Hydra. Having bought an old run-down mill, he carefully restored it and from his high perch, overlooking the port, he would keep an eagle eye on the comings and goings. How Elefteris then also became wealthy is partly mystery, partly conjecture, but wealthy he is. More famous locally for being the self-appointed "saviour" of Hydra, Elefteris's weekly routine was and still is, I believe, to travel to Piraeus to the department of building works and check out new building applications for Hydra. Copies in briefcase, he would then return to the island and set about inspecting these "works." His personal mission was to ensure that the works being carried out were exactly as per the building permit and in keeping with Hydra's strict building codes. For Elefteris, no deviation whatsoever would be acceptable. His pet hate was the building of swimming pools. I would think that having been thrown into Hydra port more than once, swimming pools presented an absolute nemesis to Mr Elefteris. Swimming pools on Hydra are prohibited. Other than the pool at the Hotel Bratsera, the ones that exist are either illegal or installed before the ban came into effect. So, you see, on Hydra, it's not only cars but also pools and even solar units on roofs that are banned. Swimming pools, it seems, use too much water and even if you want to buy the water or collect rainwater yourself in a cisterna as I do, you still cannot use this precious commodity in a pool. Swimming pools also deflect from the tradition and antiquity of the island. There is certainly a lot to be said for this local determination. It makes Hydra the most unique island in my opinion. It can have its drawbacks, too. When reading up on the history of Hydra, I discovered that the island was once the major ship-owning centre of the Mediterranean. A spinoff was the amazing mansions built by these captains of the seas. However, that was in the years when ships were powered by sails. Along came steam engines, but Hydra stuck to its tradition of sail and soon the island was left behind, overtaken by ship owners from other islands such as Syros, Chios, Andros, and so on, who had seen the future and built new ships powered by steam engines. Hydra's dominance in the shipping trade died, and the island became a virtual museum, living on its past. That traditional past was now its jewel, attracting artists and tourists alike.

Mr Elefteris was smart. He had found a niche for himself. Of course, what he wanted was for people to actually build swimming pools illegally. Then, oh my goodness—shock horror, discovering them, he would threaten the owner with exposure and court action. There was no way out for the offender and how honourable it was for Elefteris to protect Hydra from such decadent comforts of the idle rich. Except that, it seemed that a tidy sum of money could make the whole problem just disappear. I was told of one person who paid more than twenty thousand euros to turn probing eyes elsewhere. Yet another local builder who refused to pay, then found himself in court being prosecuted for an illegal swimming pool he had built for a client, had to pay a fine of ten thousand, but he kept the pool. He estimated he saved ten thousand euros than if he had passed a brown envelope to someone. I had to ask myself, does that mean that crime pays or doesn't pay? For sure, Mr Elefteris, as I was told, had friends high up in Athens and he was one local "*Malaka*" that you didn't want to cross. Plus, there was a local election for mayor coming up and Mr Elefteris had plans to replace the existing long-standing mayor. The said mayor had only just held on to his seat in the last election by no more than a dozen votes. It was going to be a battle. Whoever could secure the votes was anyone's guess. One way or another there was a lot of potential earnings at stake.

Nico of Nico's Bar was a supporter of Elefteris. Other bars and cafés were not. It seemed that depending on which political party you were in, or whom you were going to support at the next election, determined which café you patronised for your coffee and gossip. As I was now an official local resident, some stealth was required to make sure I visited the right coffee shop, as this would clearly show where my support would lie. On the other hand, I thought, best I share the love around and frequent a few different cafés for my coffee time. I didn't see why I should show my hand so openly. It was obviously going to be a huge poo fight in the local election campaign in the months to come, and I had my own challenges and Martha's House to take care of.

CHAPTER 20

The Epitelos taverna is just off the port, located behind the main church of Hydra. It's a common local meeting place for many expats. Consequently, it's not unusual to see a gaggle of English, Germans, and Americans enjoying lunch there most days. It's also a very good place to get an honest, good feed at the right price.

It was at Epitelos one evening in early summer that I met the lovely Ruby. She was on a gap year, a nice, pretty, typical gap year student from the USA. Ruby had studied the History of Art in Houston, spent the previous six months in Florence immersed in art, and had come to Hydra as she heard it was a colony for artists. I don't think Ruby could paint herself, but she certainly knew her art-talk, so she fitted in well with the local wannabe artists and the truly talented ones. Hydra does, in fact, have some very good artists, as well as dreamers. I sort of adopted Ruby, as did others. She seemed independently vulnerable, the kind of girl you just had to look after, like a streetwise cuddly kitten. After art, the next most important thing in Ruby's life appeared to be food. She seemed to be always eating. Every time she came for a social visit to Martha's House, she had one eye on the fridge. When she stayed with me for a few weeks, the only part of Ruby I saw was the back of her head as the front part was always either in the fridge or the food cupboard. More annoyingly, she never gained any weight; she was razor thin. I started to resent her.

Ruby knew how to swim, but her experience had mostly been confined to school swimming pools. As she didn't want to walk too far, her favourite swimming spot was the stunning Hydronetta to the south of the port. Hydronetta is a cool place to go. Mostly nubile young women and toned men sit under the café's umbrellas, ordering Cuban beer and exotic fruit cocktails, whilst listening to an eclectic selection of music. Below the tables and chairs tucked into the side of the rocks is a swimming platform where you can step down or dive into clear blue waters. Around the corner behind you is the port. There is always a hive of activity in the summer months with hydrofoils, private boats, and motor taxis coming and going. Not too close, but at an adequate distance to make people and boat watching a pleasurable pastime.

Born in Dallas and educated in Houston, Ruby didn't have much experience in the sea. But Hydronetta's heady mix of music, cocktails, and "Positanoesque" views could lull you into a sense of overconfidence and daring.

Having cleaned out my fridge the week before, and my refusal to restock it, Ruby had moved on to greener, more abundant food pastures at Rick the artist's house. Rick was a very social and generous American artist who had been living on Hydra for many years. I hadn't seen Ruby for a few days, until I spotted her floating on her back in the flat sea on that brilliant blue day. I was at Hydronetta, chatting away to people I had come to know, looking around at the views, saying hello to a new friend or one of my hotel guests. Every time I looked up, Ruby seemed to be floating further and further out, obviously in her own world, dreaming of Picasso or Pizza.

The stillness of the water was shattered by the arrival of the *Flying Cat* from Spetses. *Flying Cat 2* came in as usual from the left, then almost aligned with Hydronetta to enter Hydra from the port side as expected. Ruby's dreamtime was interrupted by the surge and series of waves created by this large vessel. First, Ruby was pushed back towards the rocks, and then back out again. Not that she was ever in any real danger—there are no rips or currents to speak of. But we're not talking about an experienced swimmer here. On her second or third push back to the rocks, Ruby lost it and somehow seemed to collide with one of the orange buoys outlining the swimming area. On minute she was there, the next she seemed to disappear. At that moment, a water taxi coming from Kamini to Hydra port happened to be speeding by and seemed to heading right over the top where Ruby had just been, close to the orange buoy.

I turned to one of my hotel guests, an Australian by the name of Bry, to see if he had seen what I had, but his chair was empty. I leaned over the wall on the terrace I was sitting on and looked down below to the swimming area to see Bry surfacing in the water just a few feet from where Ruby had last been seen. Up she came, being pulled up by her hair, spluttering and coughing all over Bry who had dived in to help her. It was an automatic, knee-jerk reaction I suppose. Having been brought up by the ocean in Australia, Bry had done the mandatory life-saving certificates and had spent more time than he probably should out in the surf. So, it was no big deal for him to get Ruby out. I was very proud, of course. My hotel guest was saving Ruby. I looked around at the other tables, but no one had moved. All too engrossed in their own perfectly enjoyable hedonistic world to have noticed the drama below. More bottles of beer coming out, another coffee frappe here and there, music turned up. The Hydra world just moved on. Spiros pulled up his water taxi, thinking that he had caused Ruby, now clinging to Bry, to nearly drown, he circled back and hauled them into his boat.

Ruby was grateful but embarrassed. It took some time for her breathing to return to normal, and she was shaking despite the heat. Spiro insisted he take her to the hospital on the island, not much of a hospital really, more a clinic to access whether the local pharmacy could provide adequate medical care or whether one needed to be transported to the mainland. The hospital kept Ruby in for observation overnight.

I never saw Ruby swimming again after that day. In fact, she left Hydra shortly afterward, and no one has heard from her since. Rick said he sent her an email, but it bounced back. Maybe she is on Facebook, but I doubt Rick searched.

CHAPTER 21

The Danish couple in room five were leaving early. A very nice, retired couple, they had been with me for two weeks visiting their son who had a house on the island, just relaxing in the garden, or taking walks around the island when it wasn't too hot. They were not used to rising just before dawn. Nor was I, admittedly. However, the first ferry for Piraeus was leaving at seven in the morning that day, so now and again, being up with the sparrows is a must. Andreas, our mule man, was due at a quarter past six to pack their bags on his mule and take them down to the port, with Mr. and Mrs. Andersson following behind.

The sun was just coming over the hills behind Martha's House, its rays streaming down across the house and Hydra port below, stretching out across the gulf to the Peloponnese opposite. It was blessedly cool, too. You could feel the heat starting to intensify as you stepped between shade and sun. It was definitely going to be another hot, sunny day.

The Anderssons were ready. There's something to be said about the older generation. They are nearly always more organised and on time than their youngsters. A light breakfast had been prepared for them, and I brought out some containers in case they wanted a snack with them on the ferry. It's best to have something to munch on in case it gets a bit rough out there.

The three of us were standing by the blue painted courtyard doors waiting for Andreas. A quarter past six came and went. It was just coming up to six-thirty when I called Andreas on his mobile. This was very, very unusual. Andreas was always on time; in fact, typically, he came early. So, I was starting to panic a bit. My backup plan was to wake up Bry, the Australian guest, and ask him to run down to the ferry carrying the bags. I had come to arrangement with Bry, as he had been there for so long now; in exchange for doing some of the heavier lifting and odd jobs around the place, he would get a reduced room rate. I told Mr and Mrs Andersson to head off and that all was okay, the bags would be in hot pursuit one way or another. At six forty-five, Andreas appeared. Pale, sweating, and looking extremely upset. In tow were two donkeys, not Andreas's usual mules.

"Andreas, what happened to you? Where are your mules?"

"Later, later," replied Andreas. "I'll take the bags down and come back. It has been a very difficult night!"

The Anderssons, along with their luggage, successfully boarded the ferry. I witnessed this event from the top level of Martha's House. From the second-level terrace, the "Captain's Walk" as I preferred to call it, one could observe the entirety of the harbour. I managed to watch the ferry come in from Spetses and even discern Mr and Mrs Andersson, who were being assisted by Andreas, as they climbed on board.

Ten minutes later, Andreas returned to Martha's House, leading the two small unburdened donkeys. He tied them up outside in the street before coming in to share the tale of what was probably his worst night ever.

He said it started around seven the previous evening, approximately an hour after he had returned from the harbour. As per his routine, he had escorted his two mules to the small paddock he owned at the back of Hydra town. There, he had taken off the mules' wooden saddles and striped blankets, leaving them to feed on the hay stacked in the corner. He then retreated to his house, situated near Martha's House, and was just settling down to his first main meal of the day when his younger brother, Petros, came flying in to tell him that he had just gone past the paddock and one of the mules was turning around this way and that, pounding the ground and trying to bite its own belly. Colic! The dread of any horse, mule, or donkey owner. Colic can be fatal in horses, stemming from various causes such as bad feed, contaminated water, or a build-up of stomach parasites, and usually manifests as severe pain due to blocked intestines which can often lead to death. Andreas immediately phoned the only vet on Hydra, who wasn't a qualified vet but did own a pet shop on the mainland and arranged to meet him up at the paddock. Rushing back up the hill, Andreas saw that the mule was now lying down on its side and his belly was bloated, tight and quivering. As he got closer, Andreas saw the mule's eyes congested and almost sightless. This was bad. This was Mr Super Mule. The best mule on the island. His pride and joy. The arrival of the vet-cum-pet shop owner, familiar with such conditions, was a relief. Not only were these mules like children to Andreas, but they were also his livelihood. No mules, no work! The vet injected the mule with a painkiller. "That will relax his stomach muscles Andreas and it looks like you need an injection, too." Waving the foot-long needle around, he continued, "But I don't think you would enjoy this up your arse even if you are acting like a woman." Andreas tried to calm down, but to him the painkiller didn't seem to be working. Still the mule seemed to have stopped thrashing about as much and that was more important right now. "Okay, now listen Andreas, as soon as your mule seems calmer, get him up and keep him moving. Whatever's in his stomach that's caused this needs to pass. After about an hour or two, he should be fine. And get rid of that hay in the corner; that was probably the culprit. If your mule had worms, the reaction would have been slower. And keep your other mule away from the feed, too. Cheer up; it's not the end of the world. Just make sure you give him the shits like you do me sometimes." The vet had done what was required. No operation needed, he said, the mule's heartbeat was high but tolerable. The now chuckling pet shop owner packed his bag, amused by his own jokes, and headed back down to the town. Andreas, however, found no humour in the situation as he cradled Mr Super Mule's head, stroking him and waiting for a sign that the mule was calm and out of pain. It was in this position that Mr Super Mule died. Before expiring, the mule's legs started kicking violently; the drug may have eased the pain for a while, but it likely intensified the blockage in the poor beast's stomach. Death was hard and inevitable.

So distraught was Andreas that neither he nor Petros noticed the symptoms manifesting in the other mule. That, too, was starting to gnaw at its own stomach, backing into the wooden fence and waving its head around. By midnight, both mules were dead.

Having grown up riding ponies and then horses, I was in tears as Andreas recounted his harrowing ordeal. Never one to let anyone down and serious about everything in life, he had very early that morning left his beloved, now-lost mules, to call round to a friend and borrow the two donkeys tied up at their door. All so that he could still take the Anderssons' luggage to the ferry. After our Greek coffee, he planned to return to the paddock, where the one and only municipal garbage truck, one of the few motor vehicles on the island, was scheduled to remove the mules. Andreas then had to leave for Piraeus to buy two more mules. The best ones apparently come from the island of Lesbos, something I didn't know. But the cost was high, three or four thousand euros each. Contrary to what most people think, the majority of mule drivers take very good care of their mules as they hope to have them for twenty years or more. Losing two mules in their prime was not just a tragedy, but a crime.

We both sat there for a time trying to analyse what could have caused the death. Bad water? Hay? Could they have eaten something on the way up or down the hill without him noticing? Did an animal-loving tourist give the mules something to eat, thinking they were being kind? Or, worse still, was someone jealous of Andreas and all the work he was now getting so they deliberately poisoned the mules? I never found out.

Petros stepped in to help whilst Andreas was away looking for replacement mules. You would think there would be some dignity in death, even for beasts of burden, but apparently there isn't. Petros told me the garbage collector refused to take the dead mules, claiming they were too big to dispose of. A distraught Andreas then had to buy two dozen large plastic refuse bags and borrow an electric saw. He not only had to endure the death of his animals but now also had to cut them into pieces, bag them, and arrange for the refuse truck to come back and collect them. The smell and blood were overwhelming. Andreas never spoke about the whole ordeal. Petros told me it was something his elder brother reluctantly relived in nightmares for a long time afterwards.

CHAPTER 22

I speculated whether someone could be cruel enough to have killed Andreas's mules and was retelling the story to neighbour Johannes. "How could anyone kill any animal?" I said. "Even harming them or causing them pain is totally unacceptable to me." Johannes had just come back from a walking trip to the north of the island. He hadn't been around the week before when Super Mule and his companion had died. Everyone was talking about it by now, of course, and the theories on the cause were growing more elaborate. Johannes looked a bit sheepish, and his colour had reddened somewhat. This was out of character, and I grew rather suspicious. "Johannes, what have you been up to?" I prodded. We were on my terrace having sundowners, and sitting opposite Johannes, I felt quite equal; he was so big, he towered over everyone on the island and could be quite intimidating. I knew he wouldn't knowingly hurt any animal, even though he often complained about the cats that were always coming around looking for food. I knew he regularly threw some cat-luscious food over his wall to feed his local cat colony too.

Eventually, I got the story out of him. Johannes had a local friend, Stamati, who had a shack about two hours, by foot of course, north of Hydra town. The real purpose of the shack was to serve as a refuge from his constantly nagging wife. Stamati's excuse was to go hunting, not that there is much to hunt on Hydra—maybe the odd rabbit and poor little bird. Hunting whatever little wildlife is left is still a local pastime. A very disingenuous sport in many others' opinion on the island. Johannes was not fond of hunting—quite the opposite, in fact. He knew that Stamati was a lousy shot and very unlikely to kill anything. Moreover, there was some good whisky, raki, and wine hidden away at Stamati's shack, so the thought of a long walk with an amusing companion to a place of refuge had its appeal. The two men had set off the previous week, shortly after dawn, so that most of the walk would be done and dusted before the sun's heat intensified.

After about an hour out of Hydra, the path frizzles out to a trickle. Walking as much as possible, keeping to the side of the hills, the undulating walk cuts through thorny bushes, abandoned olive trees, and prickly pear bushes. Stony and hot, it was a relief when the two men eventually reached the shack. With refreshment being the first thing on their minds, it wasn't long before both were quite merry, their thirst having been quenched by wine rather than water.

It was in this state that another Maria, known as Mad Maria, came by and found them sitting on white plastic chairs under one of the few trees near the shack.

Mad Maria was a distant relative of Stamati and owned the adjoining land. She hardly ever left the place, and anyone going up there took her some treats from town. Even though she was mostly self-sufficient, Mad Maria, who was now in her late years, had lived in the shack next door since 1945, when the Second World War had ended. Her residency there was a form of self-imposed exile due to a secret she harboured, a rare thing on this Greek island. Johannes, at this point, seemed keen on sharing the full story about Mad Maria, possibly delaying the recounting of his own darker, eventful involvements.

Her mother's father and Stamati's grandfather owned land on Hydra, an olive grove under which sheep grazed. This was where Maria had spent her early years. Whether due to a bad farming season, too much "raki" or because of Mad Maria's mother's inability to live up in the mountains any longer, Mad Maria's parents left the land and moved to the island of Aegina where her mother's family owned a house and a small piece of land growing pistachios. Life was good for little Maria. Aegina is famous for its pistachios, which are a lucrative crop to grow and greatly in demand by Greeks, used in many of the delicious little sweets and pastries they love. Then two things happened to upset her life. Firstly, a little brother was born on Aegina and he being a boy became the centre of her mother and father's life. Everyone including little Maria had now become enslaved to the brother's every wish. Maria felt she was a burden. A daughter meant that a dowry had to be provided otherwise she would never marry. A son meant continuity of the family name and honour. A son also meant that the family business could be passed on and that the son and his wife when he married, would look after the parents. But then came the Second World War. First, the Italians appeared, but they were mostly ineffective, and life carried on more or less as before. When later the Nazis appeared on Aegina, life changed dramatically for many reasons, of course. All the local produce had to delivered to the local German command centre. No more did pistachios provide a livelihood for Maria and her family. If they were lucky, they would be given back enough pistachios to eat and exchange for other foods from neighbours. Mostly, like many Greeks at that time, they were left to forage in the mountains for herbs and leaves to cook and eat. Worst of all for Maria, she had lost her place in society. From being the only child of a reasonably well-off family, carrying the nobility of also being a Hydriot, which she felt put her very much above the locals on Aegina, Maria was now the big sister of a brother-heir to a crop which they couldn't sell or eat without facing severe punishment, if not death. She had always felt rather ostracised by her peers on Aegina. Maybe that's what compelled her to try and regain her perceived control over her family and village, that drove her to walk round the little port of Perdika on Aegina that morning to the fortified Nazi anti-aircraft camp on the opposite side. There, she told the commandant that there were guns hidden in the village houses by men who wanted to steal her family's next crop of nuts.

The commandant looked at the young girl, dressed in black, like most villagers, brown-faced from the sun and grubby nails from working in the orchards. He would really have preferred to just send her on her way, but a denouncement of hidden weapons could not be ignored. The first the villagers knew of the accusation was when the troop of Nazi soldiers came marching to the village, surrounding it on all sides. Every man, woman, and child were ordered to congregate in the small square in front of the church. Even the priest was dragged away from cleaning the precious icons, to stand silent and upright in fear of what was to come next. The order was given, either bring out your hidden weapons, or if they are found by the search party which had already started to go from house to house, then the family who harboured them would be shot along with every man on the village, including the priest!

Johannes went on: the commandant didn't really intend to shoot half the village, and he was just trying to scare them. So he said. But then Johannes hated all aspects of war and wouldn't believe anyone could arbitrarily shoot a whole village. I didn't share his optimism. I was scared just listening to the tale. No guns were found, and little Maria was given what you could say was a very strong telling off by the Nazi officer before they returned to their camp. The game was up for Maria. What she thought she could achieve by doing what she did who knows? But the contempt and hatred she caused in that village is still talked about today. Her family were, of course, mortified and disgraced beyond belief. Her family, in a desperate bid to salvage their reputation, labelled her as "mad," and perhaps to avoid local reprisal, she started behaving accordingly. Maybe that stopped his daughter from suffering any locally meted-out punishment. But in making out she was mad, she started acting quite mad and it wasn't long before she became notorious as "Mad Maria." As soon as the war ended, at her family's encouragement and with no prospect of ever getting married no matter how big her dowry might have been, Mad Maria moved back to Hydra and took up residence on her father's property in the mountain where she had since stayed.

She never married and was now in her nineties, she lived on what she could eat and grow. The occasional "present" from some distant relative or passing tourist hiker that came by was a bonus. Her companions and love of her life were her cats, all big and ginger, sporting white fur above the mouth that resembled a moustache. There must have been at least ten of them, all related, of course—a pride of ginger cats, each distinct and recognisable by Mad Maria by sight.

All was well with Mad Maria and her ginger cats, until a grey tortoiseshell intruder cat turned up and started eating the gingers' food. The gingers were not used to having to defend their territory as no cat had ever entered it before. Obviously, their instinct was to protect the ginger cat lands from these unwanted intruders. So, there was a little bit of chasing and nail-scratching to start with. However, tortoiseshell cat wasn't put off; after all, there wasn't anything else to eat for miles except what Mad Maria put out for her cats. This was life or death. Tortoiseshell must have had friends, too, because Mad Maria told Stamati that it wasn't long before there were two more unwanted cats around, then four and more. These intruders were smaller than her gingers but obviously had grown up in the town and were canny street fighters. Her cats were slowly becoming outnumbered and out-classed when it came to fighting. Mad Maria's life had now altered to having to feed her cats indoors and try and get them in at night to protect them. The result being that tortoiseshell and his mates were often now perched on the roof of her little house or waiting on the surrounding stone wall for some action of sorts. Something had to be done and Stamati was a hunter, was he not? Her nephew had to kill tortoiseshell and his gang before they killed her beloved cats!

Handling a firearm is risky, even more so while intoxicated, and Stamati was very drunk. Johannes, not entirely grasping the conversation in local Greek, understood the essence of what was demanded of Stamati but felt helpless.

The shotgun was brought out and loaded. The three of them set off for Mad Maria's house. Stamati in front, Mad Maria behind moving quite fast for a woman of her age, brandishing a homemade walking stick, dressed in black from head to toe like a nun, with Johannes reluctantly taking up the rear position.

The sun was going down behind them and the shadows long. Heat from the stones was like a pizza oven just opened up, combined with the raki and wine Stamati had drunk that afternoon made him a most unreliable saviour of the Ginger Gang. The gingers were on the coveted stone wall. The Tortoiseshell Gang were moving in just as the sun was setting. The prize to steal the gingers' food and women! Tortoiseshells jumped up to the stone wall, to take the strategic position coveted by these two cat gangs, Stamati took what he thought was aim and fired. Screams and fur flew everywhere! Shot from the gun found its mark. Unfortunately, it wasn't the same mark as required by Mad Maria. He had fired too soon and too wide. Stamati had managed to do what Tortoiseshell and his gang hadn't quite yet achieved and that was killing off the Ginger Gang. Ginger fur was everywhere. Stamati had eliminated the wrong pride of pussy cats. The gingers were no more. Poor Mad Maria was distraught; she fell over wailing and crying. Stamati and Johannes had sobered up by now. Amazing what shock can do even after three bottles of homemade lethal brew.

It was left for Stamati and Johannes to bury the Ginger Gang. Mad Maria was far too upset. Stamati tried to appease her by telling her she could adopt the Tortoiseshell gang now as they were better fighters anyway and would protect her.

Johannes and Stamati came back down the mountain very early the next morning. They didn't want to risk running into Mad Maria. Fearful she might attack them; they left in silence just before dawn "in the night" as they say in Greek. It was going to be a long time before they went hunting, drinking, or shooting again.

CHAPTER 23

After all the talk of death, I needed cheering up. A friend in London wrote to me about a film she had recently seen called *Mama Mia*. In the film, the leading character had moved to a Greek island and was running a rundown hotel with her twenty-something daughter, or so the story went, more or less. As the music was all taken from Abba, I couldn't think of a better way to cheer myself up than take myself off to the movies.

I had passed the Hydra Regal a number of times, sometimes without even realising it was there—a beaded-curtained doorway with a front-facing kiosk to one side selling the usual film-food: ice cream, sweets, and popcorn. A simple board on the street promoting the night's feature films.

The film club of Hydra is not to be underestimated. Besides running the movie theatre, they organise excursions to the Ancient Epidaurus Theatre, located in the mountains opposite Hydra on the Peloponnese mainland. Supported by donations and ticket sales from the Hydra Regal, it just about manages to survive, providing key entertainment on the island. Greeks absolutely love television and film, perhaps it's a calling from the ancient Greeks from some three thousand years ago? I don't know why really but linking it to ancient Greeks seems like a good idea. Nearly every café you visit in Greece will have a television blaring, and this practise extends to bars, grocery shops, and even doctor's surgeries.

It follows, therefore, that Greeks also love going to the movies. The issue with the Hydra Regal was that the cost of renting the movies from film distributors was often too expensive to be covered by the entrance fee that could be charged. Thus, the Hydra Film Club was born. Other volunteers help out as well. In turn they get to watch a movie over and over again for free.

There was a lot of excitement that night as it was the first showing of *Mama Mia*. Interest was high as it was shot on a Greek island, so, of course, the Greeks wanted to see how they would be portrayed. As it was summer, a number of tourists were also piling in to take their seats. No seat numbers here. Typically, of Greek movie theatres in the summer, it's all outdoors. Those in the know had brought cushions, which they placed on their chosen plastic chair in the garden, which was now the summer theatre. A large screen was set, with a number of ceramic pots filled with geraniums and various cacti below, high walls on all sides. But not high enough to block out the neighbours whose balconies overlooked the Hydra Regal. They got to watch everything they wanted, plus some films they didn't care to, for nothing. Behind, up a small staircase was a deck with more chairs, mostly filled with youngsters, and behind that was the projection room where I knew my builder-cum-electrician, Penko, would be busy preparing the reels for the Hydra premiere.

It was all very exciting. I eagerly awaited the start. No ads first; I guess no one on Hydra wanted to pay for ad which would only be seen by their neighbours anyway, so straight into Abba.

I really enjoyed the movie, which surprised me, as I don't normally like musicals. I couldn't understand why my London-based friend thought there was a number of similarities between my life and that of the leading lady. Okay, I too was living on a Greek island and running a guest house. But that's where it ended.

Every now and then I looked round to see the reaction of my fellow filmgoers. Particularly when some Greek islander in the film was made to look like a real plonker, but they all laughed and seemed to be thoroughly enjoying themselves. Maybe the Greek subtitles were saying something different from what was coming out of the actors' mouths? I don't think so really, but anything is possible in Greece.

Film over, we all exited. Stopping for a chat with the local notary, the girl from the supermarket, a woman who helped at Martha's House now and again. The Hollywood Oscars couldn't possibly be better than this, could they?

I headed over to the cafés around the port. After all the excitement I needed a drink or an ice cream to calm down and cool off as even close to midnight, the temperature was still around 30C. The port was busy as usual. Even though it was late, it was the summer height of the "season." Shops were still open, cafés and restaurants busy, water-taxis were coming and going continually, and a plethora of yachts and motor cruisers were in and around the harbour. I had been on the island for a while now, so most of the locals knew who I was, likewise for me, I was starting to know them. Walking the few steps from the Hydra cinema to the port took fifteen minutes or more, only because I had to stop and greet this person and that. Finally made it to my adopted café, Akritiri, when I saw Costa and Manos seated close by at the adjoining café, Poseidon. Poseidon is the favourite of most of the mule men, the "*mularis.*" Even though I had not used Costa and Manos since that day back in February when they came uninvited to Martha's House, almost demanding I use them exclusively, we were still on speaking terms. After all, this is a small place and you couldn't afford to argue with everyone.

I sat down where I could both look out over the port and across the harbour to the lit-up mansions beautifully encircling the port scene. It was then that I noticed Costa and Manos's mules were still tied up on the lamppost opposite. The mules must have been there for six hours or so, whilst these two idiots drank whatever alcoholic brew they had made that day, taking tourists for rides round the town or overcharging for taking bags up to hotels. There was something different about Manos's mule. The tail had gone. A mule with no tail! I had to ask Manos what happened; after all, this was Hydra, and mules are very important creatures. "Eleni the hairdresser asked me for it," he replied. A strange request, I thought, and asked him why she would do that and why would he give it to her? Costa had to interrupt, "The malaka has been after her for months, thought he would impress her, so he cut the mule's tail off and gave it her. She made it into a wig, then told him to fuck off."

I only hoped she gave the mule hair a good wash before sticking the tail on her head. Poor Mule. Now, sometime later, at least its tail has grown back, but Manos still hasn't grown any brain and is still as deaf as the post the mule was tied to.

CHAPTER 24

The way up from the port to Martha's House is marked with bright white and blue signs with the name "Martha's House" and an arrow pointing up this way or that. Bry had helped put them up for me as people kept losing their way. Having been given the wooden tablets as a gift from our local carpenter, I then paid Penko the builder an enormous amount to paint them and do the sign writing. The streets of Hydra are such a labyrinth that it took me some time to find my way around when I first arrived. Not being that good with directions, for the first month, I found I was taking a slightly different way each time I went back up to Martha's House. If I found the streets and lanes confusing, then how would my guests find Martha's House? Years before, Aunt Martha had someone place the odd sign here and there, but they had mostly faded or fallen off. The solution was obvious. So, one morning, I recruited Bry the Aussie and, following the quickest, easiest path down from Martha's House to the port, armed with about a dozen wooden signs, nails, a drill, and a step ladder, removed the old signs and put up the new ones. Where it was near or on someone's house, I would knock on their door and ask them politely if I could replace the old sign. No one objected, and some even offered to help. One couple passed us and stopped to stare at us for a moment, looking quite disapproving. I said hello to them, but they snubbed me and moved on. I knew who they were. An American couple, quite rich from all accounts, had bought one of the famous old Venetian mansions up above Martha's House. They only visited Hydra for about three months of the year; the rest of the time, they lived in San Francisco where they owned an art gallery. Their house here on Hydra was filled with modern art.

The Americans' look said it all. "How could I, almost an expat of sorts, lower myself to be seen running around the island with a drill and stepladder?" Obviously, they thought I was letting the side down by doing such a menial task. I didn't care; it was quite amusing, really. Anyway, I couldn't imagine letting anyone else put up the signs. Goodness knows where they would have ended up or where they would have led our unsuspecting guests. I remember visiting Venice a few years before and seeing many signs to St Mark's Square. One set of such signs led me around and around for about an hour until I ended up in a cul-de-sac, at the end of which was a trattoria. A clever way to get business I suppose of you are off the beaten track, but I didn't want my signs to lead potential guests to another hotel, so I was quite happy to put them up myself.

Job done. I admired my signs every time I went up and down the hill. That was until I returned from my evening out at *Mama Mia*. Someone had "stolen" my arrows! Indeed, all my carefully hung signs were there, but all the arrows showing the way had been scraped off or painted over.

At first, I wondered if the sun had faded the arrows. But then, why wasn't the rest of the sign faded as well? Sabotage! Someone obviously didn't like my signs and didn't want my guests to find their way to Martha's House.

The next morning, I was out there again, painting the arrows back on and looking around to see if I could spot the culprit. I had my suspicions but couldn't prove it, of course. I would have to catch them red-handed. It didn't take long, and the shining path to

Martha's House was back on. So, I finished off the morning at Stella's fantastic little pastry shop eating *galaktoboureko*—a very traditional Greek dessert like a custard tart with syrup in filo pastry—and drinking Greek coffee. Stella said she, too, would keep a look out for the thief who obviously went around in the night armed with white spirit and paint.

The battle of the signs may have been won, but the war obviously wasn't over. That evening, I had a visit from one of our friendly local policemen. Officer Stathis was very likeable but took his job seriously. He had received a complaint from someone, unnamed, he said, who worked in the mayor's office. Our signs were too brightly coloured and too many, and this unnamed person insisted that the police make us take them all down.

"The complaint hasn't by chance come from Mr Zaloumis, whose sister-in-law happens to own the Spitaki Pension?" I couldn't help but throw the accusation at Officer Stathis. Of course, Stathis couldn't betray the source of the complaint. After some coffee, iced water, and lots of discussion on our terrace, a compromise was finally reached. I would remove about three of the signs. Thus, Officer Stathis would show that he had been round to see us and reprimanded me. He had achieved a result, of sorts. I wouldn't fall out with him because I would keep nine of the twelve signs. So, everyone would be placated. That's Democracy "Greek Style."

CHAPTER 25

Our neighbour at the rear of the building opposite, Father Charalambous is away from the island for most of the year. Lucky me! At first, when I heard there was a priest living opposite, I was quite happy. After all, people came to Hydra for the peace and quiet as much as any other irrational or rational reason. The last thing I wanted was to find that I had neighbours who perhaps played loud Greek bouzouki music every night or screamed incessantly at their children. I had, and still have, an aura of quiet and peacefulness around Martha's House. I was lucky, I thought when it came to neighbours. Until, that is, Father Charalambous returned from his monastery in the north of Greece. I had been at Martha's House for about three months before realising I had a close neighbour at all. A physical closeness due to the fact that I share a garden wall on the other side of the property overlooking this priest's house. Father Charalambous's house is very neat and tidy. I have never been inside but, looking at the property from the front, one can easily deduce that there must be two rooms upstairs and another two downstairs with a kitchen on the ground floor. The only life I ever saw at the house on a regular basis was a rather short, squat young man who turned up once a week to water the garden. Now and again, the young man would sit on the front stairs of the house, looking back at Martha's House, and if he was lucky enough, make some sort of eye contact with me so he could scowl at every given opportunity. Rather strange behaviour, I thought. But then, I was starting to become accustomed to all variations of strangeness.

My first direct contact with this young man came about in early July when an almighty storm woke me in the night. The wind was so fierce I thought I would be blown off the island and end up on the mainland opposite. The next morning, there was little damage, just buckets of leaves to be swept up and the garden tidied.

As I was sweeping up the carnage from the night of storms, I heard someone shouting at me. Looking down over the wall to the priest's house, there was the young man, dressed in the grey long frock of a church helper, almost screaming at me and waving a garden hose which had obviously become all tangled and thrown about during the night. "You, you!" he shouted up, "you have been on our land and broken our hose!" I was a bit stunned initially at this most ridiculous accusation; I told him that he must be kidding and asked him if he thought he was being funny. The response I received was more than ridiculous. "How dare you talk to me in that way?" He shouted that he was a member of the Church and the house belongs to a priest, no less, as if I didn't already know that. Apparently, I had no respect, and I was making fun of him and the house's owner, Father Charalambous, as well as laughing at the Church. I must admit, I don't take many things too seriously, but accusing me of breaking and entering, ridiculing my neighbour, whom I had never actually met, and insulting the Church, was going a bit too far. I realised this idiot just wanted an argument. Why, I didn't know, but I wasn't going to give him that pleasure. So, I just started laughing at him and called him an idiot. A silly response, I suppose; nonetheless, I should have just ignored him.

He then raised the volume of his shouting so much that a small crowd started to appear in the street. More neighbours now. What a commotion and what bad luck. One idiotic neighbour was more than enough; attracting half a dozen more was extreme. I told the idiot to grow up and went back inside. No point staying out there and having a shouting match for the neighbours to enjoy.

Later that day, whilst shopping down at the port, I made a few enquiries about the "priest boy idiot."

"Oh, you mean Father Babis and little Babis," said Mr Roussos, the owner of the largest supermarket on the island. "No," I replied, "Father Charalambous and his gardener-cum-housekeeper, the young man in the grey frock." "Yes, yes, he is Charalambous too," came the reply. "There is Father Charalambous and Baby Charalambous; we call them Papa Babis and Baby Babis that's how they are known on the island." "Babis is short for Charalambous" he went on, "there's a bit of a history there". Not another "story," I thought. Aren't there any normal people on this island? Of course not, silly me, everyone has a story here, including Father Babis.

It seems the priest used to be a *mularis*, but tending mules and carrying baggage up and down the Hydra steps was not for him. The good Father preferred to wear a skirt rather than trousers. He also had a habit of spying on neighbours, particularly those staying at Martha's House. Any kind of touchy-feely affection between a couple used to send him into a frenzy, running to the nearest church where he spent hours praying, kissing icons, arranging church flowers, and cleaning up after the real priests. Since there are over 300 churches on the island, at least four within five minutes of his and Martha's House, Father Babis didn't have far to run and hide from life, as most people know it.

He must have been around when I visited the island that fateful summer when I was a teen, but I didn't remember him and Aunt Martha never mentioned him either—not that she spoke much to me anyway. Father Babis lived with his mother, the saintly Maria, a widow of many years. It was a tradition in Maria's family that men were mularis. There could be no other career choice. Those men who dared try to run from their destiny and follow some other path ended up cursed. This Greek tradition can be scary at times. Father Babis, or just plain Babis as he was known then, was an only child and his mother expected him to carry on the family tradition.

All of Babis's male cousins were mule men, too, including Panos the Bull, who I had used in the early days to carry some building supplies up. Panos was aptly named. He resembled a gorilla and had the strength of a bull, despite drinking himself stupid every day. Panos's younger brother was also a Charalambous, the same Baby Babis. A chagrined Baby Babis was apparently destined to be a mule man, too. The two Babis shared much in common, it would seem. A dislike of hairy mule men and smelly mules was only the beginning of this strange friendship. Some thirty years apart in age, they still forged a bond, both looking for a way out of the mule business and into the Church—a holy sanctuary which to them represented cleanliness, calm, heavenly spiritualism, and the opportunity to wear frocks and huge gold crucifixes. To be Men of God was their pinnacle of life.

Many a night was spent by the two Babis, one middle-aged the other in puberty, at their local church, polishing, gossiping, praying, dreaming, and conspiring. Eventually, they both believed they found what would lead them to leave the path of the mule behind and start walking the path of the priest.

Maria died a few years before I arrived on the island. With his mother gone and as grief-stricken as he was, big Babis could now fulfil his dream. Off came his checked shirt and the well-worn baggy trousers of the *mularis*. Replaced by his grey frock of the church helper, he applied and was successfully admitted to the Greek Orthodox Church. After being ordained, he was sent to a monastery near Thessalonika. Father Babis would have apparently preferred a parish on or near Hydra. However, it seems parishes in the Greek Church are mainly reserved for married priests as it is felt they are better suited to understand their parishioners. Unmarried priests tend to live in the monasteries but can ascend to the roles such as archbishop. The Greek Church has it all worked out; one path for the married theologians leads to parish life, and the other path for the celibate leads to the top jobs at Priest Headquarters. Father Babis, not intending to marry and entering the church at the age of forty, didn't really have enough time to rise to the rank of bishop. He was content, though, as a monk on a hill somewhere in the middle of Greece. Happy anyway by all accounts, except he had left his little cousin, the Baby Babis behind. Baby Babis planned to follow in his cousin's footsteps; however, fate had dealt him a terrible blow. His father had left home some years before. There was a rumour he had disappeared to some place in South Korea to take up residence with a young maiden he had met during his occasional stints as a seaman on a Greek cargo ship. Quite a few of the locals were employed on such vessels during the winter months when mules and water taxis were not that much in demand. Baby Babis's mother, Christina, the sister of Father Babis's saintly mother, eventually obtained a divorce, which is quite acceptable in the Greek Church. Even remarriage is fine as long as you don't do it more than three times. This makes sense, I suppose, because if you get married and divorced three times, there is probably a message there that you're not very good at the whole matrimonial state, so you should probably not repeat the process.

Who divorced whom, I don't really know. However, the workings of the Greek Church were even more intriguing and complex to me. Apparently from what I understood, children of divorced parents may not, under any circumstances, become ordained priests. That was the rationale I was given as to why this young man hung around the neighbourhood, dressed like he was in the church, causing mischief. So, poor Baby Babis was dealt a heavy blow. His father had run off to South Korea or wherever; his mother was a divorcee; his brother, the hairy mule man, was mostly drunk; and his soul mate, Father Babis—the Papa Babis Nostra, as I ended up calling him—had finally made it to the monastery. However, he, Baby Babis, had been left behind. The path was blocked, and he could never cross to the other side. The best Baby Babis could now hope for was to spend his days polishing icons and cleaning the floors at the local church. The prayers of the two Babis fell on deaf ears. As a sort of compensation, Father Babis employed Baby Babis to look after his mostly abandoned house near to Martha's House, which Baby Babis did as well as any embittered person could. He had left school early to study theology, but mostly spent his time cleaning the house next door and the church around the corner. Dreams of progressing to the black frock of the ordained smashed forever, he harboured resentment towards his father, his mother, and brother. He felt jealousy that his older cousin had managed a way out, but also found solace in the name calling and ridicule he regularly received from his former school mates on the island as he swished past them in his make-believe priest's clothes. Every insult he received made him more bitter and strengthened his resolve to hate everyone else. Hate became easier then. It's difficult to be twisted if everyone is really nice to you. Baby Babis also sought solace in food, gaining more weight and attracting more attention and more insults from the other kids, which, in his mind, was a good result.

I was, of course, very receptive to the explanation—or rather, gossip—I received about Baby Babis and Father Babis. The mystery behind the morning's unprovoked hostility had been cleared up. "Oh well," I said to Mr Roussos, the supermarket owner, "I am sure that Father Babis would look kindly on his neighbours and not believe that I had broken into his house and messed around with his garden hose, God forbid!" I was positive the whole ridiculous episode would be put aside once Father Babis returned to Hydra.

I didn't have long to wait to find out. A few days later, I woke to hear the swishing of two lots of skirts, lots of patter, and lots of verbalising going on. It must have been about seven in the morning as the first of the mules had already plodded their way past about half an hour before. I knew that the mule train to the harbour always went past at six-thirty in the morning.

I sneaked out onto the back terrace, still dressed in my pyjamas, and stood as silently as possible to hear what was going on. I didn't dare get too close to the garden wall, as I thought that Father Babis, being a spiritual person and all, might sense my presence across the path that separated our houses and see me. Every now and then, I could see their two heads: Father Babis with greying long hair pulled tightly back into a small, tucked-up ponytail at the nape of his sunburnt neck, and Baby Babis with his head of thick, black, curly hair, which reached almost below his chin and covered a fair deal of his face. By the noise going on, I deduced that Baby Babis was running around their small garden, pointing out heinous crimes that he claimed I had committed during Father Babis's absence. All rubbish, of course. But then, Baby Babis was getting the attention he craved, whilst trying to emit some sort of revenge on me for my laughing at him. I knew then that there was definitely going to be confrontation at some point, as Father Babis was now getting quite wound up by the little idiot. I'm not very good in the mornings; I have to concentrate on organising the one and only member of staff I have to get breakfast out for my guests. I didn't want to get tied up in some Holy War before midday when I have more free time available. At least I knew what was coming my way. I wasn't disappointed.

After breakfast was done and dusted, I was watering the garden as usual, before it got too hot. It's something I really enjoy doing, as you can stand there for ages watering, helping your little plants grow as you look down over Hydra port and see the little boats, ferries, and fishermen come and go. It's like yoga for me. I had finished with the front terrace and given the thirsty lemon trees their daily drenching. I was by now at the back of Martha's House, where I had a number of smaller plants and where I had planted geraniums and nasturtiums, which I had brought out from England. Nasturtiums are great; they grow anywhere, and I thought they would be a great cover for the rough and stone-ridden soil below them in which they seemed to flourish. What was just a dumping yard out the back when I came was now developing into a colourful little garden, overshadowed by a large palm tree.

The only problem with the backyard was that there was little privacy. Due to the way the land is on the hill here and how Martha's House is built, the Priest's house is almost on the same level at the back as Martha's House, and whatever I did out there can be spied upon. Also, bordering the back garden is a small path than runs from the hills above Hydra down to the port. The path winds around too much for the mules, so it's really only used by locals or the occasional lost tourist. Inevitably, whenever I go out the back to water the garden or hang some washing out, one the neighbours appears to see what's going on.

So, it didn't take long for Father Babis and Baby Babis to reveal themselves to me, coming up as close as they could on their side of the small wall out the back to confront me. Both had their hands hidden in the pockets of the voluminous frocks of the priest and the church helper. Baby Babis was standing slightly behind Father Babis, partly in hiding I thought in case I attacked him and partly as he probably didn't want Father Babis to see the smirk on his face. "Good morning, Father," I said. "I am very pleased to meet my neighbour at last and to meet you in person." I was trying to be as courteous as possible, knowing that the little snake had probably told him what a bitch I was. "Good morning," came the reply in an almost high-pitched singing like voice, "I have heard much about you already and whereas I was hoping that now that Mrs Martha has left, I might have good neighbours, it doesn't seem to be that way, unfortunately!" No beating about the bush here, I thought, straight to the point our priest was, the gloves are off. "I am hoping I can be 'good' neighbours as well and that we can all respect each other." The reply I got was another slap. "It doesn't look like that to me," said Father Babis, feet now spread in a fighting stance and looking back at Baby Babis, "that you have started off respecting your neighbours. I believe that you or your housekeeper have been throwing your rubbish over the wall and even interfered with my hose!" Believe me, I was the last person who would want to interfere with his "hose" or anything else that belonged to him. I could see that this as going nowhere and surprise, surprise, at least three of the neighbours were now out in their gardens, pretending to be doing something other than gawking and enjoying the confrontation between the new *Xeni*, foreigner, and the priest. Strange thing about most people everywhere in the world, even if they don't like a priest, if there is a confrontation, they will always side with a priest rather than with the other party. So, I knew I would not be receiving any support here. "Father," I replied, "I don't know what you have been told or by whom, but I can assure that I have not been on your property, nor have I, nor anyone connected to me, interfered with any of your property. I have no interest in doing so and it would be ridiculous to think that grown-up people would act in such a way." I hoped that would be the end of it. However, Baby Babis decided to put his oar in. "You did! You did! I saw you, and you laughed at me and Father Charalambous…" spat the little idiot. The neighbours were not venturing inside from their gardens; nothing like a neighbourly fight to get everyone going. Then the attack from the rear. Baby Babis's grandmother, Mrs Eleni, lived at the back of us too. Obviously, she would want to protect her little grandson whatever the cost. "And you refused to cut back your tree, which overhangs your wall and it's killing the olive tree my poor dead saintly husband, God bless his soul, planted here on the path," she spat at my back. It was all coming out now.

Just then, my guest, Bry, appeared too; he had heard all the commotion as well. I quickly told him what was going on, by now everyone was talking very loudly, all at the same time, crazy accusations spewing out like evil gunk. Bry wasn't accustomed to how Greeks shout even during normal conversation, so having the priest, the little idiot, his grandmother, plus about three other neighbours all shouting at the same time was totally unacceptable to him, even though it wasn't actually his fight. So, he shouted back louder, in English, which, even if they didn't understand word for word, everyone got the gist of it pretty quickly. Making a direct line to Baby Babis, Bry told him that he was a liar and that he should tell the truth. To which, the good Father told me that he had known Baby Babis all his life and he was a good boy and would never lie. Babis's yaiyai, grandma, at the back, was still ranting on about her dead husband's olive tree, which I had also apparently abused, and the neighbours were arguing amongst themselves about who was lying and who wasn't. Bry started to get quite a fierce look on his face, at which point Baby Babis ran back, over the wall and hid up the path behind his yaiyai, fearing that he was going to get slapped probably. "Enough," shouted Bry, "that's it, no more talk," and he tried to drag me back inside as I was getting into the mayhem of it all too. Someone said they were going to call the police, or was it the mayor, maybe both. I wasn't sure. I told them, half in Greek and half in English, if they wanted to stand and wait for the police to come, they could do so, but I had many real things to do and wasn't going to waste my time anymore in ridiculous arguments.

I think they must have all been out the back there for about another thirty minutes, discussing who said what and who threatened whom.

I didn't hear anymore, until early the next morning, when I saw someone I recognised from the mayor's office taking photographs of our backyard. So, I went out there to find out what on earth he was doing. "I can't tell you," Mr Stratos said, "but can you come down to the town hall in about an hour." Fair enough, I thought, this must be something linked to yesterday. It was about two hours later when I turned up at the town hall offices. Amazing place, really. Located by the main church of Hydra and built in a square surrounding the church, it's a two-story building. On the lower level are what used to be monk cells, now used by the lower ranks of the municipality as storage units and offices. The is the same place where I had to get my property registered back in February of that year. Upstairs, graced by pillars all around, are more spacious rooms. In these, the mayor of Hydra has his official offices and around him are the more important local civil servants. The rooms here are spacious with large windows and the ceilings built in the traditional Hydra way, with beams interspersed by small rafters. One of the rooms I looked into whilst waiting had a very ornate ceiling, divided into squares and painted in two colours. Beautiful oil paintings of Hydra, as it was two, three, 400 years ago, adorned the walls. In truth, Hydra hasn't changed much since. Mr Stratos had a stark grey, steel desk situated just outside one of these rooms, guarding the door to the mayor's office. Eventually, he called me over and told me that he was very sorry, but the municipality had received numerous calls the previous afternoon, one call every thirty minutes in fact, complaining about me.

"What was the complaint?" I asked, as if I hadn't already guessed. Not surprising, that I had threatened young Baby Babis, that I had engaged in a dispute with our neighbour, the priest. Yet the main complaint, one so severe that Mr Stratos felt compelled to photograph evidence, was my audacity to plant flowers in my garden adjacent to municipal land. What a terrible crime it is, endeavouring to beautify the locale. Goodness me, I should be locked up.

Mr Stratos continued, even appearing embarrassed himself. The core issue, it seemed, was the potential hazard of the flower petals. If they fell, neighbours could slip on them, risking serious injury. The ultimatum was clear: I either had to uproot the plants or risk legal action should someone injure themselves. Alternatively, the municipality might remove the plants and bill me for the service. The ludicrousness of the situation painted a comical image in my mind: priests, boys in frocks, and elderly women in black attire dramatically tumbling over these petals, feigning grievous injuries to hold me accountable.

Of course, I conceded. I assured him that there would be no perilous petals overhanging onto municipal property. I half-jokingly suggested that Mr Stratos patrol Hydra to ensure no other budding horticulturist had unwittingly let any flower or bush protrude onto a municipal path, posing a potential life risk to the good citizens of Hydra. Now informed of the "rules," I was keen on ensuring that everyone on the island complied. Truthfully, I doubt my nasturtiums ever posed a genuine threat. I've largely left them untouched and, so far, haven't received any further complaints.

The priest now avoids conversing with me. Given his infrequent presence, it's hardly a concern. On the rare occasion our paths cross, I make it a point to greet him, thereby obligating a reluctant response on his part. His disdain is palpable. As for Baby Babis, he remains a looming presence, and I anticipate another altercation with him soon.

CHAPTER 26

I t turned out Baby Babis and his alcoholic brother Panos were not the only offspring in their family. Another neighbour, Athena, whom I've become rather fond of, eagerly shared more local titbits. Turning up the next day, she had heard of the neighbourhood "war," she couldn't resist visiting to spice up the narrative.

"Christina, Baby Babis's mother," she began, "received a very nasty shock years ago, just as we all did." Every time Athena visited, she brought me food from her mother-in-law, a local Hydriot who spent most of her time shopping for food and then cooking it. As Athena was quite slim and was always going on about dieting, I was of the opinion she stayed that way by dropping the various "pots" of lentils, chickpeas, beans, rice and fatty stews at Martha's House for my waistline, which was starting to expand far too much.

As I busied myself storing the day's dishes she'd brought into the fridge, she continued her story. "Christina was always a bit strange; one moment friendly, the next hurling abuse. Her sons grew up amidst these fluctuating emotions. It's no wonder Baby Babis harbours resentment towards women," said Athena, now comfortably seated on my sofa, whilst I juggled making space in the fridge for the food she had brought over. "One minute she was kissing Babis, the next beating him."

"So", I replied, "that's rather typical, isn't it? Everywhere you turn, you can hear a parent scolding their child, sometimes even hitting them over trivialities, and then, moments later, smothering them with affection and appeasing their every whim. Why would this make Baby Babis stand out? Shouldn't they all be unstable?" I fired at her.

To Athena, it seemed as though every Hydriot was unhinged, except her, of course. Ridiculous, really. But then, if I thought all this was normal, what did that make me? That's where Athena and I greatly differed as that she had blanket opinions about most things. All men are cheats and liars, all women jealous and crafty, all kids psychotic, all foreigners who lived on Hydra are drunks with too much money, and so on.

Getting back to the tale, Christina's husband used to spend the winter months working on one of the Greek cargo ships somewhere in the Far East. Christina's life started to fall apart in September 1993. That month the dry Meltemi winds from the north brought more than just dust and choppy seas; they brought two letters. The first bore a stamp unfamiliar to Christina. Even though she had seldom ventured beyond Hydra, save for the occasional trip to Ermioni on the opposite mainland for the weekly market, she recognised that the stamp was definitely not Greek. Similarly, the handwriting on the envelope addressed to her husband, Andreas Frangelos, Hydra, Greece, was foreign. Another Andreas, not to be confused with my lovely mule guy Andreas.

In typical Greek fashion, Christina didn't hesitate to open the letter clearly intended for her husband's eyes only. To her dismay, two photographs of a baby girl slipped out. Dressed in a pink ensemble, the infant appeared distinctly Asian with raven-black, straight hair, upturned eyes, and delicate features. Yet, one trait stood out in stark contrast: the baby's nose was undeniably a miniature version of her husband's, set against the backdrop of an otherwise exotic visage.

Christina's heart raced so fast that she found it hard to breathe. The letter was written in what looked to her like English, but Christina couldn't decipher it. Did she need to be punished even more by learning exactly what the letter said? Probably not, but the urge to find out whilst reaping in another layer of pain was too much to ignore. She just had to discover what the letter said. Off she went to Athena's aunt, Hera, who was the only person in the vicinity that she knew who could read English. That's how Athena learnt of the tale many years later. A frantic-looking Christina, clutching photos in one hand and the two letters, one of them opened, in the other, approached Athena's aunt. Christina demanded that the letter be read out loud but, before doing so, forced Hera to vow upon the lives of her nieces and nephews—since she had no children of her own—that she would never reveal the contents to anyone besides Christina.

Hera was reluctant. She believed it was none of her business, and she questioned the necessity of swearing upon anyone's life. However, with each passing second, Christina appeared increasingly desperate and unhinged. Hera faced a quandary: refuse and Christina would probably have a breakdown right here in front of her, or read the letter and then be a party to some sort of deception. Athena's aunt, a gentle woman not accustomed to such fuss, eventually relented. She extended her hand and Christina passed over the letter, trembling, uncertain yet anticipating its contents.

"It's from someone called Mee Jung in Korea," said Athena's aunt, "I can't tell if they are a man or a woman. It could be a man simply sending your husband a picture of his newborn baby."

"Or," spat Christina, "a woman sending my husband a picture of a baby which just happens to have a nose as ugly as his!"

Sighing, Athena's aunt felt compelled to continue reading. "Well, okay then, maybe you are right. The nose does look familiar, I must admit. But it's certainly not ugly. The letter says how much Mee Jung misses Andreas and that it has been a very difficult time in Busan over the past year. However, it has all been worth it now that she has given birth to…"

At this point, Hera paused, bracing herself and Christina for the subsequent revelation.

"Given birth to their beautiful baby girl whom she has named Gini Mee Jung, after Andreas's mother, whom he told her was called Virginia."

By this point, Christina had turned quite pale. The tan and wrinkles from her weather-beaten face had almost vanished; she was in deep shock. Christina stood up and extended her trembling hand for the letter and photos. There was no need to know more; enough had been revealed. "This letter never arrived and you never read it," she warned. "If you tell anyone—anyone at all—about this, then you have to admit that you are as guilty as I am for opening it." Every word was enunciated with the precision of a hammer hitting a nail. Christina prepared to leave, she tore the letter and photos into shreds with her dry, trembling hands. Exiting Hera's residence, she approached the communal rubbish bin situated between their two houses, opened the lid, and discarded the remnants. Following that, she opened the second letter. There was no need for a translator this time, as it was in Greek. It contained an offer from the shipping company for Andreas to return to sea again for the coming winter. There was a repeat job offer: he would be flown to Seoul and then join up with the other officers and crew before joining the ship at the port of Busan. Busan! Home to this Mee Jung and now this baby Gini Mee Jung. That letter was quickly dealt with too. Torn up and thrown into the bin after the baby photos. Then, as calmly as she could, Christina adjusted her skirt, collected herself, and proceeded to her home, where no mention would ever be made of the two letters that came with the Meltemi.

However, Athena's aunt could not just let it go at that. She had always wanted a child, but her husband had died young, leaving her to care for his parents. The dowry she brought into the marriage was quickly eaten up taking care of her in-laws and herself. No dowry, no marriage. That was the way it was in Greece then, and it remains the case in some instances even today. So, despite being attractive and somewhat educated, Athena's aunt faced a future confined to the modest home of her in-laws, caring for them until they either passed away or she did. The picture of the darling little babe, swathed in pink, featuring an exotic face, full lips, and a distinctive nose, tugged at her heartstrings. This was the child she never had, and she couldn't bear to see it discarded into the municipal rubbish bin. Thus, the photos were rescued. Pieces torn apart by hate were that night put back together by love. A blemished picture of a baby was carefully placed into the back of the old photo album she cherished. There it remained, a secret treasure, a photo of a child that Athena's aunt would caress and speak to over the ensuing years as if it were her own.

Andreas was to remain oblivious to the existence of his daughter in South Korea, and of the letters. More correspondence from the shipping company and Mee Jung followed, meeting the same fate until they eventually stopped. That winter was challenging as there was no extra money, as were the subsequent winters. However, for Christina, the lack of extra money was a small sacrifice to pay to ensure her husband wouldn't be lured back to that foreign land, possibly to father more children with Mee Jung.

The secret lay buried for nearly a decade. Yet, like all secrets, they inevitably emerge into the light. Which is what happened when Athena's aunt Hera died. At the time, Athena was in Cyprus visiting other relatives. She had shared a special bond with her aunt. It wasn't difficult for the police to locate Athena's mobile number and deliver the bad news. Within twenty-four hours, Athena was back on

Hydra at her aunt's house. With no formal mortuary on the island, her auntie had been taken to the hospital and placed in a coffin there. The funeral was to be held the following day. Baby Babis had found Athena's aunt dead. When he visited her home to borrow a pot for his mother, he fled in horror. The neighbours, sensing the tragedy that had befallen the quaint house that had been Athena's aunts since her wedding in the 1950s, gathered in commiseration. Before dying, she had written out her wishes: the house and all its contents were to be bequeathed to Athena, her favourite niece. The sole exception was a photo album, which she left to Andreas, her cherished neighbour and cousin's husband.

A strange bequest, many thought. However, the wishes of the deceased had to be honoured. Andreas arrived at the house to help Athena. They had to sort through old clothes, shoes, newspapers, and drawers filled with blue plastic shopping bags. On the small table beside the tall, hardback chair where the aunt used to sit for hours reading and reminiscing, lay the photo album.

"Auntie Hera wanted you to have this Andreas," said Athena. "I don't know why. Perhaps because there are some photos in it of your father with Auntie's father-in-law from before the war." Andreas wasn't particularly interested in old photo albums, but out of respect for the old lady, he felt he should at least pick it up. Flicking through, he saw mostly black-and-white photos from fifty or more years ago. In one or two, he recognised his father as a young man. Three-quarters of the way through, the album ran out of photos, except for the last page. Probably because it had been turned so many times, the album naturally opened to this last page, revealing the only colour photos within. Two pictures of a little baby with jagged edges; a photo that had been torn apart and then obviously pieced back together, much like a broken china vase. For Andreas, there was something hauntingly familiar about the face. Did he recognise himself or someone else? Whatever the resemblance, it

129

was enough for him to try and remove the photo. As he did, it began to crumble in his hands, revealing faint writing on the back: "To Andreas, Gini Mee Jung, born 27 August 1993, Love, Mee Jung." The revelation was so shocking and perplexing that Andreas found himself sinking into auntie's most uncomfortable chair. He stared at the fragments in his hand, his mind racing. How could this photo, of a baby with a woman he had known many years before in South Korea, be here in this album, in his now-dead neighbour's house? It made no sense. A loud buzzing sound filled his ears as if he might faint.

All this time, Athena had been moving about the house, sorting out what should be given away, thrown out, or retained out of respect for her aunt. She hadn't really noticed what Andreas was up to, just glad he was there, as she didn't want to be in the house on her own. However, she soon noticed Andreas, who was now like a zombie, completely dumbstruck. "How did your aunt get this photo?" he hoarsely whispered to Athena. Athena had no idea. She herself had never looked through the album. It was mostly full of dead people and that made her uneasy, so she left it well alone. Looking at the torn fragments in Andrea's hand she couldn't really make out who exactly the photo was of. Another, similar photo remained adhered to the album. For the first time, Athena closely examined the torn image, seeing it was of a baby, dressed in pink with unmistakable Asian features. Japanese or Chinese, perhaps?

Andreas must have begun piecing things together. He stiffly placed the torn photo in his pocket, ripped the last page with the other photo out of the album, and walked out. From the door, Athena watched him walk home, just a few steps down the hill. Shortly after, she heard shouting, followed by wailing, and then a woman's scream that sounded like pure agony. A door was forcefully slammed shut.

Looking out, Athena saw Andreas dressed for a journey, small bag in one hand and his bouzouki in the other, walking resolutely down the hill. It was nearing six pm and the last ferry for Piraeus was due to depart soon. Strange, she thought, one minute he was here helping me, and now he has decided to go to Piraeus. And why would Andreas take his beloved bouzouki with him, the only thing he seemed to love other than smoking cigarettes? He was well known on Hydra for his musical skills and was in great demand for major festivities, as well as impromptu, raki-fuelled evenings, when music and dance broke out.

As Athena didn't like to stay in the house on her own anyway, especially now that it was getting dark, she decided to go to Christina's and find out what was going on. She knocked on the door. Even though she could hear movements of someone on the other side of the door, no one answered. On Hydra, people rarely lock their doors even today, so opening the door carefully, Athena went in to find Christina sitting on a kitchen chair, elbows on the table, hands spread wide, shoved up into her hair just staring at nothing. "Your aunt betrayed me," said Christina without even looking up. "She said she would never tell but she broke her promise. I curse her as she has now cursed me." Horrified that someone would curse her dead aunt, who was not yet even buried, Athena turned on Christina, shaking her and demanding to know what the hell was going on. Christina just stared, lips tight and mean, her little face even more pasty than ever. Baby Babis then made his presence obvious. "Your aunt read the letter from father's *boutana* in Korea. There was a baby, the *boutana* said it was father's bastard and was going to blackmail him. Mother threw it all away to save father any anguish. Now your aunt has come back from the grave and told him, so he has left us and said he is never coming back."

Indeed, Andreas never did come back. Rumours suggested he went back to Korea to see his daughter, who by then would have been around ten years old. Or perhaps he went anywhere to get away from his wife who had lied to him for years. After all, he had also lied to Christina. He was no saint. Wherever he went and what exactly happened between Christina and Andreas, Athena never knew. Only that Christina later obtained a divorce, which then prevented Baby Babis from entering the Church. It also resulted in Christina hating Athena to this day as she blamed Athena's aunt Hera for Andreas's departure.

Baby Babis was full of hate anyway. He never really liked it when his father was home. The two of them never got on, and his father's presence took his mother's attention away from him. He resented how his mother would oscillate between berating him and then showering him with affection. He loathed Athena and her deceased aunt, blaming them for his father's departure and his subsequent inability to become a priest. Above all, he detested Mee Jung and her daughter, Gini Mee Jung, who, if the unread letter to his father was to be believed, was his half-sister. How bewildering it was for a Greek boy on an island to have a half-sister who looked entirely different and lived halfway across the world!

What all this had to do with my planting a few flowers behind Martha's House, I was not sure. But my life and the life of this young man were now connected in a way and through this drama I had come to know of Mee Jung and little Gini Mee Jung, who might even have more brother or sisters by now, all half-Korean half-Hydriot.

CHAPTER 27

Athena ended up with the album, except for the last page, of course. She told me she didn't stay in her aunt's house that night. In fact, she never spent even one night there after that day. Not until about five years later, when she had enough money to have the old house totally renovated. I don't believe Athena was trying to erase the memories of her dead relatives through renovations. Rather, she was scared of them, terrified of anything associated with death and particularly by what she felt was a ghostly presence in the house. This fear is the reason she never really perused the photo album. There were photos of dead people in there and that unnerved her. However, not wanting to simply discard the album, she handed it to the young man next door, Yanni, who was about eighteen then and had a passion for photography. His other love was working at the local Hydra cinema where he endured selling tickets and sweets, just so he could spend as much time as possible watching movies and learning how Penko the projectionist did his job. Even just looking at a reel of film made him feel good, as his imagination blossomed under the perception of many stories and adventures those reels held. Athena thought that being such a photo buff, Yanni might appreciate the old photos in the album and some of them were relatives of Yanni anyway. In any case, the album had at least ten blank, thick black pages. Yanni may be able to do something creative, thought Athena. It was a shame to just throw the album in the bin even though it gave her the shivers. Creativity was exactly what Yanni did but maybe not what Athena had in mind, otherwise she wouldn't have just given the album away.

Athena's other aunt, Poppy by name, ignited Yanni's passion for photography. Poppy and Hera were sisters. During the Second World War, Poppy acquired a camera. A rare and coveted possession, it was a German-made Balda Juwella box camera. How Poppy came to possess the camera was unknown to Athena. Regardless, Poppy skilfully used it, with the photos she took and developed placed in her sister Hera's album. Most of the photos in the album from the 1940s and 1950s were captured with that Balda Juwella. Athena had seen the camera once, mistakenly thinking Aunt Poppy had salvaged it from Hydra's rubbish dump. The ultimate fate of the Balda Juwella remained a mystery to Athena. The camera's true value lay in its captured memories.

As Yanni perused the old album, he immediately recognised its chronological significance. The album essentially chronicled Aunt Poppy's life and that of Hydra. The photographic journey began with family snapshots from the mid-1930s, showed a noticeable gap during the turbulent war years of the early 1940s and the subsequent Greek civil war—likely due to the discouraged practice of photography and the scarcity of film—and resumed around 1948, depicting church processions, Easter celebrations, and a wedding at the church in Kaimini. None of that was much to excite Yanni. He recognised a face here or there of some neighbour or relative. Marching in front of the church on national days, groups of family members sitting in cafés after a baptism, posed photos on the rocks overlooking the port of Hydra. There were a few interesting photos of fishermen sorting out their nets and of the little cacique sailing boats during the annual Miaoulia festival. Turning the next page, Yanni hit upon Aunt Poppy's camera work in what must have been around 1957. There, over the next three pages, were some of the most exceptional photos Yanni had ever seen in his little life. One photo after another of Sophia Loren and other actors, taken right here on Hydra. Well, of course, it couldn't be anything else other than during the time when *Boy on a Dolphin* was filmed on the island. Yanni knew very well the story of the Hollywood crowd all coming to Hydra to make the film. His in-depth film knowledge gained by working at the local cinema and listening to locals retelling old stories of who had been gathered up as film extras or handymen building some of the sets.

But these were no ordinary photographs. Even if taken by an amateur—likely Aunt Poppy, given she was among the few with a camera at the time—the photographs brilliantly showcased a radiant, young Sophia Loren. One photo captured her at the port outside Spyros café, while others depicted Sophia with her mother, notably in a car, on the port—the island's sole paved road back then. Another of Sophia and her mother leisurely browsing Hydra's shops. All very natural but posed beautifully. No wonder Sophia Loren became a world-famous star, thought Yanni. He knew by his film history that it was her first American film. Her launch into Hollywood and even in these little personal photos in this album, the Italian star-in-waiting was absolutely stunning.

There were other photos too of various celebrities visiting the island. Even a few of the old King Paul, father of the then exiled King Constantine of Greece.

Yanni held little regard for the monarchy, past or present. After all, he was born after the last King of Greece left for exile in 1973. To him, the photos of monarchs alongside archbishops touring Hydra were of historical interest rather than the allure of Hollywood, and thus less captivating.

Yanni knew there was no future on Hydra for him. He wanted to go to America and study cinematography in Hollywood-a dream he had harboured since he was about ten. Staying on Hydra his future at best would be working in a bar or café and hanging out at the rooftop open air cinema during the summer. Maybe if he was lucky, catching a girl with a dowry, which included a piece of land or a little house for them to live in. But now with this treasure trove of a photo album, maybe he could earn enough to buy a ticket out of here. Why not? Others had escaped. Indeed, Hydriots had been travellers for centuries, turning up in the most unusual places even as part of the first fleet of convicts sent to Australia.

Inspired, Yanni decided to sell the photos. He believed there had to be someone who would appreciate their value as much as he did. His aim was to raise enough money for a ticket to New York, where a distant uncle, who owned a restaurant in Astoria, resided. From there, he'd find his way to Los Angeles. Having saved up 500 US dollars, he saw this as his golden opportunity to gather the rest of the funds he needed.

After about three months, Yanni's confidence of getting rich through the photos was beginning to wane. He had written letters, in poor Greek, to various magazines in Athens offering them the opportunity to the photos. To his dismay, he received not a single response.

It was only by luck, as most things are in life, that one day when he was working at his café job, he started to talk to Ute, a German lady who had lived on the island for years and years. Ute was tall and elegant. A severe bob hair cut framed her once perfectly symmetrical face. By then in her seventies at least, the bob now graced an interesting, well-wrinkled and well-travelled face. If the stories were to be believed, Ute was once a very successful film director. Yanni wasn't privy to the specifics of her career, but he considered her the closest connection he had to "Hollywood." As he served Ute her usual order—a 'metrio', medium sweet Greek coffee, a glass of warm milk on the side, and a piece of rather dry sponge cake—he glimpsed the title of the book she was engrossed in.

Then, as his eyes settled on the photo gracing the cover, his interest was sealed. It depicted none other than Sophia Loren, posing provocatively, in a yellow dress that looked as if it had been soaked through and shrunk at least two dress sizes, clinging to her voluptuous figure.

This was his chance. Obviously, Ute was into film and intrigued by Sophia Loren. Surely, she of all people would appreciate the beauty and value of his photos. He had never actually spoken to Ute. Worse, this strange lady made him rather nervous. Ute surrounded herself with an eclectic group of people. Most of her foreign visitors were gay men. All quite smart, smelling of expensive colognes, usually engaged in what seemed to Yanni as educated and knowledgeable conversations whilst they sat with Ute at her favourite cafés around Hydra's port. When Ute's gay friends were not visiting, she herself loved to party with the young men of Hydra. Yanni had witnessed it all at the café where he worked. When she was in the mood, and not engaged in reading a book or a back issue of *Spiegel*, bought from the local and only newspaper shop on the island, Ute would start chatting with the group of predominantly Albanian young men that hung around the same cafés. For these young men, an evening at a local bar, talking, smoking, watching football on the huge flat screen TVs, or sneaking smouldering looks at the girls, all for the price of a coffee, was their best option for entertainment. Ute had quite a reputation with the young lads. Most of them had taken turns in engaging in some sort of flirtation with her. Several had reciprocated her flirtations, even accepting invitations to her hilltop house for drinks. The specifics of these encounters remained a mystery to Yanni, but it often resulted in the lad-of-the-hour arriving the next day, pockets deepened by at least a hundred euros, treating his mates to drinks. This generosity was typically accompanied by a barrage of cheeky jokes about the previous night's escapades. Despite the morning-after ribbing, many had visited Ute's residence and reaped the financial rewards.

Currently back indoors, Yanni stood by the bar, anxiously awaiting the next order so he could serve a table near Ute. As he drummed his fingers, craving a cigarette, he pondered how to broach the subject with Ute without her misconstruing his intentions. Being the first local Hydriot—not an Albanian—to visit her residence would set tongues wagging. Everyone would be privy before he even set foot inside, and his island reputation could be irreparably damaged. He needed to garner her attention subtly, ensuring she didn't perceive any ulterior motive—and most crucially, without any desperation for her hundred euros.

Having delivered the Nescafe frappe to the table just past Ute's, Yanni saw his chance. "She was here, you know, right at these cafés, standing almost where you are now sitting," he began. Ute hadn't realised at first that Yanni was talking to her and had carried on reading, so she had only caught the last few words. Their conversation unfolded in English—Yanni with his broken limited English and Ute with her far superior vocabulary marred by a heavy German accent. "Who was here, Yanni? What are you taking about?" she queried.

"Sophia, of course!" he almost shouted back at her, standing over her table, "Sophia Loren stood right here where you are sitting." Ute was intrigued. How did this young man know Sophia had been there, especially since the star had visited in 1957, long before Yanni's birth? "How do you know that Yanni? You weren't even born then."

Seizing the moment, Yanni retorted, "I have the photo, a real one taken by my aunt. Actually, I have many photos of her from the fifties and of other celebrities on Hydra. My Uncle Stamati confirmed it.

He was about twelve at the time and they used him as an extra in the film."

Ute's curiosity peaked. She wanted to know everything, how he got the photos, did he have the negatives, who took them and when, how come Yanni had them and so on. However, Yanni could see that they were attracting too much attention from fellow customers. "I can bring them down tomorrow Mrs Ute if you would like to see them. I won't have much time as I'm going to take them to Athens as someone wants to buy them, but if you come by Isalos café by the ferry stop tomorrow at ten in the morning, I can show them to you before they leave the island, probably forever."

Yanni felt a mixture of triumph and trepidation. He had been forthright with Ute, which was a departure from her usual interactions with the smooth-talking young Albanians. Yet, Ute's interest wasn't just personal; she contemplated selling the photos to her publishing contacts in Germany. She envisioned a feature in magazines like *Paris Match* or *Der Spiegel*, with a potential spotlight on her and her Hydra residence. Selling the house had been on her mind, and this opportunity could be a gamechanger.

At ten sharp the next morning, Ute navigated the lanes from her hillside house to the port. Turning right past the sequence of cafés, banks, and tourist shops, she rounded the other side of Hydra's horseshoe harbour. She spotted Yanni seated among the water taxi drivers, sipping coffee. Beside him was a sports bag, and on the neighbouring chair, a large brown envelope. Yanni's hand rested protectively atop the envelope, signalling to Ute that it likely contained the prized photographs.

Smiling at everyone seated around the small table, primarily the captains of the various water taxis bobbing up and down nearby, Ute greeted them warmly. Turning to Yanni, who was seated with his back to her, she said, "Kalimera, Yanni, I see you are ready for your trip. Do you want to discuss that little business before you go or are you too busy? No problem if you don't." Ute could play it cool too if she wanted. After all she hadn't got where she was by being a wallflower.

"Kalimera, Mrs Ute," Yanni responded, "I'm waiting for the ferry from Spetses, then it's off to Piraeus or wherever the day takes me. But I do have time to chat. Let's sit closer to the ferry terminal; I don't want to miss it." Yanni stood, and with the envelope and holdall in hand, Ute followed him.

Getting straight to the point, Yanni stated, "I want 5,000 euros for the photos, or they're going to Athens."

Ute, always the shrewd negotiator, retorted, "Yanni, if they're as fascinating as you say, I'll offer 2,500 euros now, finalising the deal. But this is on the condition that there are no copies. Anywhere. If you want more, take them to Athens. Best of luck."

This was not exactly what Yanni was expecting. The night before, the old bag was drooling at the mouth for the photos, now she was acting like she was doing him a favour by taking them off his hands. He needed at least 5,000 euros for his U.S. trip and Film School ambitions. He had found he had another distant cousin in California and had written to him already. His cousin would, he was positive, take him in and offer him food and lodging until he got on his feet. That was the Greek way and even if they were now second or third generation Greek, they would stick to the traditions and offer whatever hospitality they could to a fellow compatriot and family. Still, 2,500 euros wasn't going to get him far. "Mrs Ute, that's an insult to me and to Sophia herself. Even if I hadn't been made a better offer, there is no way I could sell these unique and precious historical records, which is what they are, not just photos, at such a price. They are original and there are no copies. My aunt took them in the 1950s and no one has seen them outside the family."

The two were now at an impasse. With time ticking away, Yanni had a mere thirty to forty minutes to clinch the deal before he boarded the ferry. Silence enveloped them. Both lit up cigarettes, their exhales almost confrontational in the still air. The atmosphere was thick with tension, each waiting for the other to make the next move.

After some negotiations, a Greek extra sweet coffee for Yanni and a freshly squeezed fruit juice for Ute, they settled on a price of 2,950 euros. Ute made her way to the Alpha bank on the corner to withdraw the money, while Yanni, pleased with himself for striking a deal, pondered how he would adjust his expenses to achieve his aspirations.

The *Flying Cat* arrived punctually. A few passengers from Spetses disembarked, while many from Hydra boarded, Yanni among them, now holding just his holdall. Ute confidently strode back across the harbour with the envelope of photos tucked securely under her arm, mentally preparing her marketing and press campaign.

As he boarded, Yanni received a smattering of farewells. "Just off to Athens for a few days," was his casual reply. Some of the mule drivers, anticipating potential customers disembarking, cheekily teased him with innuendos about his upcoming escapades in Athens. As the vessel's ramp rose, the *Flying Cat* set off, swiftly exiting the quaint ancient harbour en route to Piraeus. Meanwhile, Ute meticulously crafted her promotional plan at home, surrounded by her newly-acquired photographs. Before she could finalise her strategy, Yanni had bypassed central Athens and was aboard a bus to Athens' El Venizelos International Airport. His journey to Hollywood had begun! He made a personal vow: he'd only return to Hydra aboard a motor yacht, grander than the ferry he had just departed. Anything less would be a failure.

Athena hadn't heard from Yanni in the many years since he had left the island. All she knew was that he made as far as New York and worked for an uncle at his restaurant in Astoria. She hoped he had fulfilled some of his dreams at least.

CHAPTER 28

Ihad nearly forgotten about the incident with Mr Elefteris—aptly named *freedom*—and his unfortunate dive into the harbour. Martha's House needed some external repairs. The wooden railing of the upper terrace had been smashed, all thanks to a young German guest who had been staying with his inattentive mother. Shockingly, I caught the boy swinging from the electric wires that ran above the terrace. Horrified, I screamed at him to stop. How he managed to reach them was beyond me. His must have dropped onto to them from some higher place. His mother, obviously quite used to his pranks, was in her own little old world. Drinking wine and reading magazines on the terrace while the boy was playing out his Tarzan fantasy. In his fear, the boy swung abruptly, crashing into the wooden railings. I managed to grab him by his shorts, preventing a potential tumble over the garden wall which would have resulted in a two-metre drop. It was baffling how he hadn't broken the electric wires, risking electrocution.

The entire garden railing had to be replaced. It was going to be a big job. I got on the phone to Penko and asked him to order some wood and get a new railing made. It was imperative to have it fixed soon; anyone lounging on the upper terrace risked falling onto the alley below, aptly named for the occasional donkey droppings.

It wasn't the best job, but five days later, I had a garden rail back up. A few days after that, Mr Elefteris showed up. "I see you have been making building improvements," he says. What the fuck! How did anyone know or even care about my wooden rail? "You should have obtained a building permit first," he continued. I challenged his interest in the matter. He declared himself the protector of Hydra and stated that anyone attempting to alter this archaeological historical site would face the law. I questioned whether it was better to leave a potential hazard than fix something broken. Apparently, it was, and unless I removed the rail, the police would be notified. I basically told him to fuck off. My mistake.

A few days later, a representative from the Archaeological Service, a branch of the Greek Ministry of Culture, turned up at my door, accompanied by none other than Mr Elefteris and a policeman. They served me with a court summons, and Officer Stathis was instructed to escort me to the police station to be charged with damaging an archaeological site—a serious offence, it seemed. I contacted my lawyer, Mr Condos—Aunt Martha's lawyer, to be precise. He spoke to the ministry official, conversed with the policeman, and then relayed the situation to me. According to him, our victory was that Officer Stathis agreed not to handcuff me as I went to the police station; I could go voluntarily to be officially charged. This, in his view, was a satisfactory outcome. Obviously, Condos and I had divergent views on what constituted success. He instructed me to contact him after the charge was filed.

My walk to the police station drew a fair amount of attention. I had never been charged with any offence anywhere in the world, so this was a totally new experience for me. Mr Elefteris gloated from my terrace as I was escorted away. I also passed Baby Babis, who seemed equally delighted at the sight of my quasi-arrest. The ministry's representative maintained a stern, official demeanour throughout. At the police station, I was shown to one of the two cells. Thankfully, they left the cell door unlocked. They offered me water and even inquired if I wanted coffee. My priority was my guests at Martha's House, so I urged them to expedite the procedure. After reading me the charge, which I said I understood but didn't really, then having me sign a document, I was free to leave—for the moment.

A few days later, Condos turned up. It was all my fault, apparently; I should have obtained a work permit before I repaired the rail, rather than risk a guest breaking their neck. Since I hadn't, I should have discreetly passed a *fakelaki*, or brown envelope, to an undisclosed person instead of resorting to expletives. The result was an impending court case and an inevitable fine. However, he assured me he would handle everything—for a fee, naturally.

Did I learn my lesson? Probably not. As it wouldn't be my last run in with Mr Freedom. Now that I had come to his attention, he wasn't going to let it rest.

By the time I returned to Martha's House, Katerina had cleared up breakfast, cleaned the guest rooms, and was hanging out the laundry. Waiting for me were Athena and Aphrodite. "Oh, Zoe, we feel sorry for you. That bastard Elefteris," they exclaimed in unison. "We all hate him on this island," they told me. "He was thrown off Poros where he tried the same thing and he came here to fuck us off. He is not one of us; he is not a true Hydriot. Someone should make sure he gets thrown in the harbour again permanently. Don't worry," they said. They reassured me, "We'll sign a witness statement asserting that you had to repair the rail. Otherwise, people, including the vital tourists that this island relies on, could have been killed or injured. It was essential." Just then, Andreas appeared with his new Lesbos mule parked nearby. He'd just been to the police station with his brothers, hoping to demand my release. They were disappointed to find I'd already been freed, and they'd missed out on the action.

145

Feeling frustrated, I mentioned considering shutting the place down. Their response was passionate, urging me to continue despite the troubles, as I brought tourists and added value to the community. That night, as I settled into bed, I felt heartened. I might've lost the day's battle with Mr Freedom, but I was gaining support from my new found Hydra family.

CHAPTER 29

As I only offered breakfast at Martha's House, my evenings were free, and going to the cinema had become one of my favourite pastimes. The Hydra Regal was now my main source of entertainment and solace. I'd learnt from regulars to bring a comfortable cushion and a *"packeto"* (takeaway) from one of the cafés before entering. Armed with my *"packeto"* of frappe and *spanokoptika,* I settled in for the best that Hollywood could send to Hydra.

It had been billed as the premiere of the year, and there was an unusually long queue. That surprised me. If not for Penko, my trusty builder and the cinema's projectionist, I doubt I would've secured a seat that night.

There was a lot of excitement and chitchat amongst the locals. What is going on, I thought. As the film began, focused on a drug gang near the US-Mexican border attempting to infiltrate a local community, there was silence. Thwarting the gang was a US ranger: a tall, dark, swarthy, and striking young man, alternating between riding a horse and a mule laden with seized contraband.

When he first appeared on the screen, there was a huge gasp from the audience. He was undeniably handsome, but I couldn't understand what all the fuss was about. He must be famous, I thought. Not that I would know.

My life had completely turned upside down nine months before and I wasn't up to the usual celebrity gossip one reads in the red top newspapers and gossip magazines. Our hero certainly had a look about him that I recognised. I had seen young men on Hydra with the same sort of swarthy looks, but not as handsome as this actor. I didn't hang about for the credits. As soon as the film ended, I left. It had been another long day, and I was eager to get to bed.

A few days later, there was another new film playing at the Hydra Regal. Off I went again, picking up my *packeto* from my favourite café before heading in to claim my reserved seat this time. It was fortunate I had pre-booked, as eager filmgoers were queued up again.

It was a war film set in Afghanistan and there was our hero again. He was now an elite soldier, stranded alone on some rocky barren hilltop, no water, few bullets and had to make his escape back to his army unit. The rocky terrains and mistrustful villagers posed no significant obstacle for our hero. Each of his appearances on-screen elicited gasps from the audience. The film was engaging enough, and as its final scene played out, I hastened my exit. My rear was now completely numb from the uncomfortable plastic seating. On my way out, I checked the billboard to identify this captivating actor: John Stephan. His name didn't ring a bell, but he seemed poised to become as famous as Johnny Depp or Leonardo DiCaprio. Over the next few weeks, John's films continued to be a feature until the summer cinema closed at August's end.

Menalous, who overall managed the esteemed Hydra Film Club and the Hydra Regal, culminated the season by organising an excursion to the ancient theatre of Epidavros on the mainland Peloponnese, opposite Hydra. Sadly, I couldn't join due to my commitments at Martha's House. Nonetheless, several of my guests participated and shared that it was a wonderful evening.

CHAPTER 30

That morning, Mr and Mrs Simonds from Adelaide, Australia, checked in. They were keen on retracing the footsteps of renowned Australian authors, George Johnston and Charmian Clift. Aside from a vague memory of a book from my mother's bookstore in England titled *My Brother Jack* and the tragic end of Charmian Clift, who took her life in Australia just before the release of Johnston's *Clean Straw for Nothing*, my knowledge about them was limited. Apparently, Johnston's book would reveal all about her affairs whilst on Hydra. Not that Johnston had been that monogamous from what I had read years ago.

Meanwhile, I was becoming quite familiar with Leonard Cohen's exploits on Hydra. George and Charmian were contemporaries of Cohen, and there were whispers that Clift and Cohen had a brief affair. Given the stories of rampant drug use and intimate liaisons amongst the expatriate literary crowd on Hydra in the 1960s, any accurate recollection of events might have blurred over time.

Before climbing up to Martha's House, Mr and Mrs Simonds spent the morning wandering around the port, searching for the house that the Johnstons had lived in during their hectic decade on Hydra during the 1950s and early 1960s. They had been going around in circles, they said, and hadn't located it. *Did I know where it was? What about Leonard Cohen's place?* By then, I had hosted several

'Cohenite' guests and was well-acquainted with Cohen's house, just a short distance from Martha's House. However, regarding Johnston and Clift, I was clueless about their residence. My Aunt Martha had lived on the island during the bohemian era's zenith when Hydra attracted a slew of primarily impoverished artists, who found it a conducive environment to nurture their creativity, and that too at a minimal cost. Times had evolved significantly since. I wished Aunt Martha had maintained and bequeathed a diary. Martha's House contained numerous potential hiding spots for such a treasure, and I hoped to discover it during a comprehensive search someday.

I told the Simonds that I was due to go down to the port soon and would locate the "Johnston-Clift" home and take them there later that evening or the following day. In the meantime, they could stroll by Leonard Cohen's house and stand under the banana tree overhanging from his garden wall. Personally, I found nothing particularly striking about Cohen's house, and it barely offered a glimpse of the sea or port. However, one of the world's most respected artists had lived there and his family still owned it. Its history was undoubtedly one of Hydra's major attractions.

The Simonds seemed taken aback by my unfamiliarity with the dwellings of Hydra's famed foreign residents. In their eyes, Hydra's reputation rested on luminaries like George Johnston, Charmian Clift, Leonard Cohen, Axel Jensen, and Marianne.

I found it intriguing that they attributed Hydra's contemporary allure solely to the bohemian influx of the 1950s and 1960s. Undoubtedly, their perspective of Hydra's essence diverged from the island's educational narratives and contrasted with local Hydriots' pride. Their idealised perception illuminated for me the existence of two parallel universes on the island: one being indifferent to the other and one oblivious of the other. Interacting closely with locals in my business endeavours, I perceived Hydra differently from many of my compatriots. For Hydriots, iconic figures from the Greek War of Independence, such as Andreas Miaoulis and Lazaros Koundouriotis, stood tall. The Koundouriotis Mansion, donated by his family as a museum, remains a significant edifice on Hydra. When thinking of artists, most Hydriots would likely recall Panayiotis Tetsis, whose residence was virtually next door to Cohen's. Additionally, other notable Greeks, including Boudouris, Kriezis, Tsamado, and Voulgaris, hold special places in their hearts.

There was a long list of Greek and Hydriot heroes with whom the local community associated their history and development. Out of all the expatriate artists that lived on Hydra during that brief bohemian period, I'd argue that Cohen is the most respected and remembered. His family still has connections to the island to this day. I can't recall any other artist for whom a street was renamed or a bench placed in their memory overlooking the Argo-Saronic.

This isn't to diminish the contributions of the artists who came to this island and flourished creatively. In many locals' eyes, these foreign artists absorbed from Hydra and gave to the rest of the world, rather than contributing significantly to Hydra itself. Their legacy will likely endure well beyond the island, if not directly on it. And if it brings in throngs of tourists every year, so much the better.

CHAPTER 31

My primary reason for heading down to the port after breakfast was to coordinate the mule delivery of floor tiles to replace broken ones in two of the bathrooms. Given my prior encounter with the police and Mr Freedom, I secured what's called a minor building permit for the task. Once Andreas and his reliable mules dispatched the tiles from the cargo boat, I planned to begin the quest to locate the house where George Johnston and Charmian Clift lived in the 1950s.

Penko, the Bulgarian builder, was up at Martha's House awaiting the delivery of the floor tiles and he knew what needed to be done. No need for me to rush back this morning.

After a few coffees at Pirate Bar and garnering enough information from its patrons—along with a heap of unnecessary gossip about Hydra's antics in the 1950s and 1960s—I managed to identify two houses the famous Australian writers had apparently rented during their years on the island. Engrossed in finding the house where they once wrote, drank, bickered, and had affairs some sixty-plus years ago, I was nearly bowled over by four men ferrying another man on what seemed like a sun lounge cushion. It eerily resembled one of my own blue and white striped long cushions. Sprawled on the cushion with a hand clamped over where an ear should've been was one of Penko's labourers.

What the hell! I watched the group hastily move towards the island hospital. I immediately shelved my search for the Johnston residence and hurried back to Martha's House. Arriving there, I found Penko cleaning up shattered tiles in the street just beneath my garden wall. Two others scoured the street, apparently searching for something. "Hey Penko," I exclaimed in my now breathless bad Greek, "what the hell happened here?" Through a series of emphatic hand gestures, Penko recounted the incidents that unfolded while I was leisurely enjoying my coffee and the local chitchat at the port.

Apparently, instead of carrying in the tiles in small bundles from the street to Martha's House, the guys decided to tie some rope around them and haul them over the garden wall. However, the rope wasn't strong enough and the tiles were too heavy. The horrific outcome was the rope snapping, sending the tiles crashing to the street below. Worse still, the rope took part of Arvi's ear with it. Now, the rest of Penko's men were scouring the street for the ear.

And yes, that was my cushion being used as a stretcher. They couldn't think of anything else to use to transport poor Arvi to the hospital. Just then, both Penko's mobile and mine rang. We each received updates about the situation at the port. I was not sure whose news was graver.

Penko learned that the local hospital couldn't do much for Arvi. They were transferring him to Piraeus by ferry for treatment at a mainland hospital. My call was from Mr Condos, my lawyer. It's seldom good news when he calls. Mr Elefteris, though absent from the island, had been informed by a watchman down at the port about the incident. He'd called the local police, who were now on their way up to Martha's House. Likely to arrest me again, I thought. To add insult to injury, the bastard Elefteris had also phoned my lawyer to keep him in the loop, no doubt gloating.

It wasn't exactly an arrest this time, but rather a warning. They'd been informed by someone in high places, Elefteris no doubt, that I was making illegal repairs on my property. Additionally, I was accused of employing illegal migrants, one of whom now only had one ear. If these claims were true, the ramifications could be dire, especially for me.

Fortunately indeed, I had secured that "small works permit." The looming question was whether the authorities would consider tile replacement a minor job or deem it major reconstruction. If it was the latter, I was in the shit again.

As for the now one-eared Arvi, I explained to the charming police officer that I hadn't hired him. My contractor was Penko and he wasn't illegal. What Arvi was doing on my property I had no idea, so best talk to Penko. Nothing like passing the buck. It was Penko's problem now if he was employing illegal immigrants and if said illegals had lost an ear in the process. At least, it got me out of jail this time. Hopefully.

The police asked to see my small works permit. I was relieved to have had the forethought this time to get one and I proudly handed it over. They then called down to the police station to verify, they said. As they thought, it wasn't valid because I was supposed to lodge it with the police before the works were started. It was missing a "stamp." Another procedural hurdle I was unaware of. Remarkably, I was starting to get quite good at this, getting myself in the pooh bin and dodging bullets. I explained that I was en route to the police station with the building permit when I was summoned home due to their impending visit. Not wholly truthful, but thus far, complete honesty hadn't done me any favours. Further, I told them that no work had started, so no offence had occurred. I could see the scepticism on the police officer's faces. They then had to make another call to the police chief down at the port; he was probably enjoying a coffee break at one of the cafés down there. The police chief wasn't totally convinced and decided that Penko and I should accompany the officers to the station. No handcuffs were used, which was standard practice, but we were given no choice. It was either accompany them willingly or face consequences.

I was getting used to the Hydra police station by now—almost a second home. For someone who had previously had minimal encounters with the police, here I was, once again, facing allegations of potentially damaging an archaeological site. In layman's terms, this meant nearly replacing bathroom tiles and, depending on the report from the hospital in Piraeus, potentially being charged with the injury or even manslaughter of a now one-eared illegal immigrant. My arrest record seemed to grow more intricate with each visit. Naturally, my legal expenses would likely follow suit.

I recalled a Greek friend from Athens mentioning years ago that while individuals outside Greece typically have a regular doctor, in Greece one tends to have a lawyer. I had to place yet another call to Mr Condos, anticipating another impending court case. Meanwhile, they confiscated my building permit, stating they might consider endorsing it. Only if it returned with all appropriate approvals would I be permitted to order tiles from Athens and organise the required works.

I was feeling pretty exhausted by the time I got out of there. Penko was more rattled than I was. His past experience with police stations in Bulgaria probably had something to do with that. We were both concerned about poor Arvi as well. A few calls later as we made our way back to Martha's House, we found that Arvi had been stitched up and as soon as he was fit enough, he was being put on a bus back to Albania. His career as a builder's apprentice on Hydra over before it had even started. Obviously, I was obliged to cough up some money to compensate him and I pressured Penko to do the same. I wasn't of the opinion that I was totally to blame for Arvi's loss of bodily part and earnings; after all, Penko employed him and was there supervising.

Upon reaching the house, I checked in with the Simonds, who were relishing freshly squeezed orange juice on the upper terrace. Fortunately, they hadn't witnessed much of the day's events. Even if they had, I hoped they wouldn't have grasped the full extent of the situation.

The Simonds seemed more eager to inquire about the Johnston and Clift house yet again. I confirmed that I had located it and offered to guide them there the following morning. I advised them to simply relax and soak in the terrace views. "Oh yes," Mr Simonds remarked, "sitting here, I can see why you chose Hydra over England. You're truly living the dream."

For a moment, I just stared back, lost for words for once. Living the dream? That was me, supposedly living the dream. Not.

CHAPTER 32

"Why me?" I lamented to Spyros, who ran a taverna near Martha's House. Why was I drawing all this unwanted attention from the police, that pest Elefteris, and the hostility from neighbours? "Because, my dear Zoe, you came here and started a business. That's why," Spyros replied. He was at the back of the taverna in his kitchen, preparing the fish, octopus, and prawns he had caught on his early morning fishing expedition. "You're not being singled out. You're being treated just like the rest of us, striving to carve out a living on this barren rock, catering to a brief tourist season." Perhaps I faced a tad more pressure, he continued, given that I wasn't born on the island nor schooled here, meaning I'd never be accepted as a local. Or did I assume that as a foreigner, I deserved special treatment?

Spyros, being from a long line of Hydra families, faced no such challenges. However, his wife, Soula, hailed from Tinos in the Cyclades. "We've been married for ten years, and people still ask why I chose her," he shared, now scaling the fish with added gusto. Soula entered at that moment, having dropped their daughter at the nearby pre-school. She managed the "front of house" at the taverna and had a strong, albeit occasionally challenging, personality. Spyros chose to remain in the background, cooking and occasionally shouting back at her if she made an error or failed to respond quickly enough when he rang the service bell. Soula never hesitated to respond in kind. I had great affection for them both; they had become a form of therapy for me. I frequently dropped by their taverna after my morning errands in the port—sometimes for a coffee, which they reserved for a select few, occasionally for lunch, and every so often for dinner. How Spyros managed to serve fifty to a hundred dishes during each seating from that minuscule, sweltering kitchen was a Greek marvel to me.

"They label me 'the catholiki' because I'm from Tinos, and my mother was one of the final students at the Catholic Ursuline School there," Soula shared. I had once visited Tinos on a day trip from nearby Mykonos, primarily to see Tinos's renowned Greek Orthodox cathedral, the Panaghia Evangelistria—a significant pilgrimage site for Greeks. My knowledge was limited, so I asked Soula to elaborate. It seems Tinos has a pronounced Catholic heritage, with several Catholic churches. Catholics and Greek Orthodox living harmoniously side by side. Once, the island's population comprised seventy percent Catholics, with the remainder being Greek Orthodox. Today, the numbers have flipped. The Ursuline School began as a girls' orphanage, aiming to educate and equip them with life skills. Such was the school's reputation that, over time, many affluent Greeks sent their daughters there for education. Graduates became highly sought-after for marriage, being well-educated and often bilingual. The school finally closed it's doors around 1988. Nowadays, it operates as a museum, and annual Catholic services still take place in its church. Soula's family hailed from a village in the interior of Tinos, near the now-closed Catholic school. Her father, a teacher, was Greek Orthodox, while her mother was a Catholic descendant of the Gyzis family, which had inhabited Tinos and nearby Cycladic islands since the time of the Crusades. Although Soula was baptised at the Greek Orthodox cathedral on Tinos, she was regarded as a Catholic on Hydra. To her, it seemed as if being Catholic was a tarnished term. So much so that when their daughter was born and they wished for a baptism in the local church, the priest began questioning Soula's faith. Ever passionate and fiercely proud of her heritage, Soula promptly picked up little Maria and took her to Tinos for the baptism.

"The local priest missed out," Soula declared sharply. "We paid a bigger price," retorted Spyro. "It would have been more economical to make the 'donation' here than to journey all the way to your village on Tinos. Plus, we still had to hand over a hefty 'fakelaki.'"

Anticipating a typical heated argument between the two, I felt it best to shift the conversation's focus. Other foreigners seemed to come here, rent or purchase property, and appeared to live an idyllic life without the daily challenges I faced. "Not true," countered Spyro. "They either feign ignorance, or even though some have resided here for decades, they don't grasp Greek, leaving them oblivious to their surroundings. All seems well," he noted, "until they attempt to sell their property. They might then discover that their building is unauthorised, its size exceeds what was recorded at the old land registry, or basement rooms, 'apotheki' in Greek, intended for storage, have been transformed into illegal living spaces. Often, a portion of the land might belong to the neighbouring family, who, after willingly selling years ago, may now challenge property boundaries." "It's a nationwide issue," added Soula. "This happens throughout Greece, not just on Hydra. You could live in a house for twenty years, then spend another twenty attempting to legalise it for resale. Alternatively, one might simply bequeath it to a relative, passing on the complications and debt."

The happy life solution seemed to be to buy and never sell. Maybe that's why I had met so many here who said they were packing up and moving elsewhere, yet they remained put. Maybe Aunt Martha had come to the same conclusion when she decided to "gift" Martha's House to me.

"We're all in violation," declared Spyros. "Greek law is framed that way. We're born in contravention, we die in contravention, and we're deemed guilty until proven otherwise."

So very true, I thought. That's life here. I could either accept it or keep moaning about and never move on.

CHAPTER 33

The Contessa lived on my street, but about a hundred steps further up. I adored her house. She'd owned it for over thirty years and had fully renovated the place. It was a sea of white, from the shutters to the stone floors and terrace, to the furniture. However, standing out were two elaborately carved large doors, painted in an array of blues, pinks, greens, and reds. These doors were propped up in her garden, somewhat obscured and in stark contrast with the rest of the Contessa's home.

"They're from Peru," the Contessa remarked, noticing my fascination during a recent coffee invitation in her garden. I expressed my admiration for them, mentioning the perfect spot I had at Martha's House between my living area and kitchen, which had been devoid of doors since my arrival. The Contessa's collection spanned artefacts from across the globe. Most resided in her "apotheki", basement, except those aligning with her white aesthetic. Her affinity for white remained a mystery, especially given her colourful life. Born in Italy, she married a diplomat, living in numerous locales, predominantly in Asia and South America. Along her travels, she amassed, or was gifted, various artisan keepsakes–like the Peruvian doors.

Those doors captivated me. I wanted those doors and was upset they were rotting away in a corner of her garden, unadmired and unloved.

A few weeks later, Roland another artist, this time from Poland, who'd lived on the island for years, dropped by. Roland had been pressuring me for some time to give him a room and some space in my garden so he could paint. He could be "my artist in residence," he said, and in return for free board and keep, his painting would, he was adamant, attract many guests and I would benefit for very little effort. The house wasn't quite big enough to accommodate an artist in residence. And I needed the income the room could give me, so I turned down his generous request over and over again.

I braced myself for another plea as he walked in that day. To my surprise, he bore a message from the Contessa: I could procure the Peruvian doors for 500 euros, provided I arranged their transport. The Contessa was departing for her villa in Venice soon and wouldn't return until the next summer. The sum was hefty for me, yet procuring and shipping new doors from the mainland might have exceeded this. Besides, these weren't just any doors; they hailed from Peru. Roland specified cash payment, which he'd relay to the Contessa, and I could then retrieve the doors. With the agreement sealed, I contacted Andreas, my mule man, to arrange collection for the next day.

Come morning, Andreas appeared with two mules and the two prized doors. How he navigated them down from the Contessa's residence and through tight turns without damage was beyond me. Nevertheless, he seemed none too pleased. He revealed that he was actually a carpenter and couldn't fathom why I'd want these old doors when he could have crafted new ones for me. I too was somewhat bewildered by my impulsive purchase. Andreas, already disgruntled about my acquisition of the doors, realised they wouldn't fit through the street entrance. They were simply too large. Our options were limited: either enlist additional help to hoist them over the garden wall or manoeuvre them through the upper-level back door. However, a tree in my inner courtyard blocked that back entrance. Andreas outright refused the latter option, asserting the route was "cursed". "Bad luck. Anything you usher beneath that tree will bring misfortune," he elaborated. This superstition seemed uncharacteristic of Andreas, a younger fellow whom I hadn't associated with the traditional beliefs about bad luck or the "evil eye" held by many villagers. Stubborn as his mules, he wouldn't relent. Eventually, Andreas called in reinforcements, deciding more hands were needed to transport the doors over the garden wall. Furthermore, he pointed out that the doors were infested with woodworm and required treatment before installation. "I warned you," he said, "you keep walking under that tree at the back and this is what happens." Once the doors were in my garden, at least, I asked Andreas what he was going on about as it was getting on my nerves now. All this talk of cursed trees.

He began recounting the tale of an another American couple who'd resided further uphill. Their residence, in proximity to the Contessa's, was nestled a few steps higher, beyond old stone archways. Once a hub for opulent gatherings and art showcases, the place now stood almost forsaken, its windows boarded. A caretaker would sporadically air out the property and maintain the garden terraces. Although I was uncertain about the owners' fates, I understood a relative from New York had inherited the estate. Throughout my eight months on Hydra, I hadn't crossed paths with them.

According to local lore, during the couple's tenure on Hydra, they, along with their circle, embraced an esoteric sun-worshipping faith. This wasn't mere yoga or dawn rituals, which, to the astonishment of many, the Greek church still views with suspicion, equating it to some form of devil worship. This was more cult-like, drawing a varied crowd, including some deeply troubled souls. Among them was a young woman who often dressed as a nun. Andreas wasn't sure of her origins but was certain she wasn't Greek. He was a young lad at the time, assisting his father with mule tasks and their family carpentry venture. Tragically, it was young Andreas who discovered the woman, hanging from a branch of the tree in my garden that extended to the street. Despite his best efforts, he couldn't save her. In the aftermath, the American couple vacated the island.

This was indeed a sad tale. My perception of that tree irrevocably changed, and I diligently trimmed any branches that overhung into the street. I was wary of the evil eye and didn't want a recurrence of any such unsettling incidents. "Their house was cursed," declared Andreas. The erstwhile caretaker had hastily departed after a disconcerting experience. Upon his routine visit for maintenance, he had entered the primary living room, which featured a massive fireplace. After aerating the room, as he exited, a raucous commotion drew him back. He was confronted with a room where every shutter was now shut, every cupboard agape, and the previously neatly stacked firewood in the fireplace, was now haphazardly strewn about the room's centre. "Evil spirits dwell there," Andreas sombrely proclaimed.

Increasingly, I began to rue the acquisition of the Peruvian doors. The financial drain of transporting them, followed by necessary woodworm treatments and then framing them for installation, was escalating. Regardless, I dispatched an email to the Contessa, expressing gratitude for her beautiful doors. I informed her of my payment to Roland but refrained from detailing the ensuing complications. Her subsequent reply was disconcerting. She was clueless about my mention of 500 euros and conveyed that she had instructed Roland to notify me that the doors were gratis, provided I collected them within a stipulated two-day window due to her impending departure for Venice.

CHAPTER 34

The sultry intensity of August waned, with the refreshing Meltemi winds extending their embrace into September. This cooling reprieve was coupled with a noticeable reduction in tourists as summer vacations concluded. Consequently, vacancies emerged at Martha's House. A few weeks prior, an enchanting Irishman, blessed with a sonorous voice and captivating green eyes, had graced Hydra. Regrettably, I was fully booked, so I directed him to Johannes, who sporadically rented out rooms—given he took a liking to the lodger, and they showcased a decent tolerance for alcohol. The arrangement was that Padraig as he was called, would stay with Johannes and breakfast at Martha's House. After some weeks with Johannes, enjoying breakfast at my establishment, he inquired about the availability of a spacious, luminous top-floor room. While Pádraig had appreciated his stay with Johannes, he yearned for solitude from the habitual sunset soirees and ceaseless camaraderie. He was a writer, on a mission to conclude a project. For him, I would have gladly sourced a room. Reallocating him to my prime room entailed some adjustments to existing reservations. Still, the prospect of having him at Martha's House now that I had a vacancy was too enticing to pass up. Naturally, he could stay.

September continued to be eventful. A booking materialised from Los Angeles, California, for a Miss G. Mullins, requesting a single room with an en suite for a five-night stay. Subsequent to this, I dispatched Andreas to the port, both to welcome Miss Mullins and to fetch some provisions I'd telephonically ordered from Roussos supermarket.

I stood by the front door awaiting Andreas's arrival. On his approach, I queried about Miss Mullins. "She's just behind," he remarked, his eyes gleaming with admiration. Curious about his gleeful state, I prodded further. "She's beautiful," he confessed, clearly smitten. "Tall, with an incredible figure, long black hair, and a face like a model's. I reckon she's from Thailand," he ventured, though given he'd never left Greece, his claim seemed purely speculative.

Moments later, Miss Mullins gracefully ascended the final steps towards Martha's House. Concealed under a Panama hat, her head was bowed, rendering her features hidden. Nonetheless, her poised demeanour hinted at a statuesque, elegant figure. As she reached eye level, her astounding beauty became evident, confirming Andreas's raving description. She appeared to be in her late twenties, exuding a model-like aura. Her features suggested Eurasian descent, though the purported Thai connection remained elusive.

"Welcome to Martha's House. I'm Zoe," I greeted, ushering her in and proffering a refreshing beverage while Andreas attended to her luggage. "I'm Gini," she responded warmly, "I'm truly delighted to be here, finally."

CHAPTER 35

Gini Mullins. The name rang a bell. Surely, she must be a known figure, I pondered. Fortuitously, I'd allocated one of the more refined rooms for her. Gini, upon being acquainted with her quarters, expressed a desire for some respite following her arduous travel itinerary spanning Los Angeles, Vancouver, New York, Athens, and finally, Hydra. She hinted at needing local guidance later on. Assuring her of my availability, I cemented my role as a hospitable host.

Later that evening, Gini emerged from her room, seeking my company in my cosy living room-cum-kitchen. She admitted to unintentionally oversleeping. I was just about to indulge in a local dish, a gift from Athena courtesy of her mother-in-law. Sensing Gini might be too fatigued for a descent to the port, I extended an invitation to dine with me. As our conversation ebbed and flowed, Gini's curiosity about Hydra, my reasons for being here, and the island's residents became evident. She eventually enquired about a local church named Aghios Andreas. Indeed, such a church stood in proximity to Martha's House. It had historical significance, having been established by a ship's captain years ago and now only opened intermittently. Her final query was about the Frangelos family. The revelation left me gobsmacked. The Frangelos were Baby Babis's kin, notably his father, Andreas, who had left the island roughly fifteen years prior, before my arrival.

Suddenly, Athena's recount from months past reverberated in my mind. Andreas Frangelos's liaison with a Korean woman who had later sent photos of a baby, Gini Mee Jung. Could this poised young woman be that very baby? Realisation hit me like a ton of bricks; her presence could potentially stir a hornet's nest on Hydra, especially since Andreas's estranged wife, the mother of Baby Babis, still resided on the island. Literally a few steps from Martha's House, this brewing situation required the utmost tact. My natural response was to enlist Athena's diplomatic skills; my own efforts in such matters were historically questionable, evidenced by the garden rail fiasco. Athena, undoubtedly, would know the right course of action.

I made some excuse to Gini and went to the front street door to meet Athena. I had to warn her about what was about to explode. Athena, hearing the angst in my voice when I had called her on her mobile, was there in a few minutes. When I told her who I thought was sitting in my living room, she nearly passed out. Athena was only distantly related to the Frangelos family and Christina Frangelos still blamed her and her deceased aunt for Andreas walking out on them. We were both trembling from excitement and terror. What could we say to Gini? There was absolutely no way Christina nor Gini's probable half-brother Baby Babis would be receiving her with open arms.

I have to admit Athena handled the whole situation extremely well. Far better than I would have. She came in and gave Gini a big hug and told her it was marvellous she was asking about the Frangelos family. Unfortunately, Andreas Frangelos had left the island about fifteen years ago and nobody had seen him since. Athena didn't know what happened. What a strange thing for Gini to turn up here asking about him? It was now Gini's turn to open up and she did.

Gini was born in Busan, South Korea. Athena and I had already come to that conclusion. She didn't remember much of her baby years in South Korea. When she was about four years old, her mother met a Canadian at a Christian mission centre. They fell in love and Gini and her mum moved to Vancouver with her now-stepdad. Gini came to think of Fred Mullins as her father. When she was about eleven years old, a funny little man appeared at her school asking about her. The teachers were very suspicious, and they called Mrs Mullins, the former Mee Jung, to come to the school. Gini wasn't sure exactly what was said at that meeting in the school principal's office. But sometime later, her mother came and took her hand and led her and this strange man outside where Fred Mullins had now arrived. They all got in Fred's car and went back the Mullins house. It was there that Gini's mum explained to Gini that this strange man, Andreas, was in fact her biological father. Andreas had been looking for them for over a year, first having travelled to Busan where eventually he tracked her to the Christian mission. It was there he was told that Mee Jung had married and moved to Canada. Eventually, he made it to Vancouver. With the assistance of the local Greek Orthodox church and a branch of the South Korean Christian mission in Vancouver, he finally managed to find out where Gini went to school, and here he was in South Vancouver. His search had now ended. However, the reunion wasn't the joyous reconciliation he'd envisioned. It became evident that Mee Jung had built a new life and Gini was contentedly ensconced in her new family setting. What could Andreas offer them both? Not much. He was getting too old to return to sea, and even if he did, it wouldn't constitute a family life. All he could manage was to work as a sailor and send back pay cheques. Taking them to Hydra wasn't a viable option either; how would they adapt, and what sort of future would Gini have on a Greek island?

It was futile. However, he had seen Gini with his own eyes and she was a shining light. It had been worth it. The loss, the journey, and now the finale of the journey. Fred, Gini's stepfather, was very empathetic, but there was no way he was going to give up his cherished family. They were happy in Vancouver. Gini was happy and content. She had a future there.

All Andreas requested was to ensure that Gini knew about her Hydriot heritage. He hoped she would one day visit Hydra to connect with her roots. Fred assured him they'd honour that wish, but emphasised Gini needed to grow up undisturbed, as a part of her Canadian family. At eighteen, she could decide whether to explore her past, a past that belonged more to Andreas than to Gini.

Andreas begrudgingly agreed and then it was time for him leave. Mee Jung and Gini watched him go. It was a cold and grey day as Andreas set off down the tree-lined street in that South Vancouver suburb. He had a long walk ahead of him. But he was used to walking; after all, he came from an island with no cars. Where he went, they didn't know. Gini received some postcards and her mother received bank transfers occasionally. Not a lot of money, but enough to pay for little Gini's music lessons. Gini finished high school in Vancouver and was offered a place at the prestigious USC Thornton School of Music in Los Angeles, California.

She blossomed as a violinist, and after graduation, her dreams materialised when she secured a junior position in the Los Angeles Philharmonic, inspired by the renowned Chinese-American violinist, Suli Xue.

Now twenty-seven, Gini had been prompted to set off for this journey of discovery after receiving yet another postcard, this time of Hydra. It had been sent to her mother's house in Vancouver and Mee Jung sent it on to Gini in Los Angeles. The postage stamp read Rotterdam, Netherlands, so it wasn't posted in Greece. Gini assumed her biological father, Andreas, had gone back to sea after all. But whether he was still alive, Gini had no idea as the postage stamp was dated many months before.

Gini retrieved the postcard from her purse, showing Athena and me. The picturesque Hydra harbour image was unmistakable, with the clock tower poised centrally. The handwritten note on the back simply read, "From your father, Andreas." This postcard was the catalyst that brought her to this beautiful island.

Athena carefully avoided telling Gini about the rest of the Frangelos family. There was nothing to be gained there. However, it was agreed that the next day Athena would take Gini on a walk around Hydra and show her the place of her father's birth.

CHAPTER 36

The Meltemi winds of September brought the third surprise: the grandest of them all. We were all quite used to seeing luxury yachts in the harbour, moored just beyond outside the port if they were too large or if space was unavailable.

You can't prebook a space in Hydra port. There's a strict port pecking order, which, while not controlled by the port police, is certainly enforced by them. The harbour has dedicated areas for water-taxis, fishing boats, larger water buses bound for the island's beaches, and areas for the ferries and hydrofoils. To secure a coveted spot in the harbour for a multi-million-dollar super yacht, its best to have a direct line to Harris, the unofficial harbour master.

For years, Harris had expertly directed the sea arrivals of the jet set visiting Hydra. Bypassing him could lead to inconvenient mooring spots, where yacht lines could become tangled and chaotic. The savvy knew to call Harris first—assuming they had his elusive number.

Harris received a call, not from a regular but from another super yacht's captain who had managed to acquire Harris's number. They'd be arriving the next day, requesting space for their Benetti super yacht. Unfazed, Harris confirmed space in the new outer moorings, specifically designed for such luxury vessels, given Hydra's rising popularity among the elite.

Athena and Gini had finished their little tour of Hydra. Gini had seen where Andreas went to school, church, his favourite taverna, and café. Avoiding his actual former house where Christina Frangelos and Baby Babis still lived. The two ladies now sat centre stage right in front of one of Hydra's busy cafés. Watching the bustling port and all the activity. A people watcher's paradise. From the south, the direction of Spetses, came a beautiful white and blue beast of a super yacht. Three decks and bigger than the hydrofoil ferry that goes to Piraeus. Athena had seen Harris go down to the outer moorings and was talking intensely on his mobile, probably to the captain of this new smart floating palace. Harris nodded at Athena as he went past, staring more than necessary at Gini who was looking quite lovely and certainly beyond the norm with her exotic features in her cream-coloured wide pant suit and cut-away top, sleek shiny black hair falling to her waist. Massive gold earrings were her only item of jewellery, matching her low-slung gold sandals. Gini didn't need make-up; she just shone in a very natural way.

The new floating palace reversed in and moored. It had taken some thirty minutes to watch it all unfold. But who was in a rush, Athena and Gini were happy sitting there as spectators. Smartly clad crew in blue-and-white shorts and polo shirts finished tying her up and the large gang plank was electronically extended. Most of the super yachts coming to Hydra were well known by name as well. No one chatting at the bars and tavernas watching seemed to know this new arrival. Then someone read out her name, which had now been somewhat obscured by the gang plank.

Sophia.

Harris had disappeared on board, a rarity as these super yachts rarely permitted locals aboard, with many employing crew and sometimes even armed guards to keep onlookers at a distance.

Soon after, Harris disembarked. As he passed by Athena and Gini, Athena's curiosity got the better of her. "Who does the *Sophia* belong to?" she inquired. Harris, typically tight-lipped about such details, seemed compelled to share on this occasion. He leaned in and whispered, "It belongs to the famous Hollywood actor, John Stephan. He's here scouting locations for a movie about Leonard Cohen." Noticing Athena's bewilderment, he added, "But you probably remember him as your cousin Yanni Stefanakis."

Athena was even more dumbstruck than she had been the day before when Gini turned up on the island. The *Sophia* belonged to Yanni, the young lad who years ago she had given that photo album to, just before he had left the island and gone to America? Yanni was the famous new actor from Hollywood that everyone was talking about. Impossible. She had to go and investigate for herself. Collecting Gini, she jumped up and started walking the two of them to the *Sophia*.

Strategically, Athena reckoned that Gini's striking appearance might increase their chances of gaining access. As they approached the gangplank, two crew members moved to intercept them. A slightly apprehensive Gini lingered a step behind, oblivious to who John or Yanni Stefanakis even was.

Asserting herself, Athena declared, "We are John Stephan's cousins. We'd like to see him, so please let us aboard." She was determined to find out the truth. One of the crew members, a blonde young man with an American accent, communicated with the captain via radio. To him, neither of the women resembled Mr Stephan. After an anxious wait, his radio crackled with a response: "Welcome onboard."

CHAPTER 37

I t was about nine in the evening when I started to worry. I hadn't seen Athena and Gini since they left around ten in the morning. My mind starting over-speculating. Had they run into Baby Babis or his brother Panos, maybe even their mother Christina and recognised Gini, or her nose, as their half-sister? Surely, if there had been some commotion down at the port, I would have heard about it by now. I called Athena on her mobile. She didn't pick up but called me back soon after. The background noise was terrible. Yes, they were fine. They were on a boat in the harbour, everything was okay, and they were catching up with old friends. I could tell that Athena didn't want to share too much as there was obviously a group of people around her.

Relieved, I set about securing everything for the night and prepping for the morning breakfast. I reminded Athena to inform Gini about entering Martha's House in case the main door was locked. I had observed several boats entering the port that day. One was massive, boasting three decks. Its unique design made it stand out. I wondered which boat they were on — certainly not that colossal one, probably one of the smaller caiques. Exhausted from another eventful day, I soon went to bed.

The next morning, breakfast was its usual mix of hustle for Katerina and me, while the guests enjoyed a relaxed meal. Bry, the Aussie, was still here, as was Pádraig, who no longer had the long trek from Johannes's place since he had settled in comfortably at Martha's House.

But no Gini. Strange, I thought, she should have been up by now.

By eleven, I decided to wrap up breakfast. Still no sign of Gini. I knocked on her door. No response. I retrieved the spare key, knocked again, and in customary hotel manner announced, "Housekeeping!" The room was empty, looking untouched from the previous day. Concerned, I headed to my living room to call Athena, hoping she might have some information about Gini's whereabouts.

Just as I was about to call, Gini walked in, impeccably dressed as she had been the day before. She didn't linger long, only stopping to apologise for missing breakfast and to inform me she was checking out. She was full of praise for the hotel and me, but she had met a distant cousin she hadn't realised existed. This cousin, also visiting Hydra, had invited her aboard his yacht for a cruise to Monte Carlo. John, her newly discovered distant relative who was also based in Los Angeles, was attending a gala event at the Opera Garnier in Monaco and had extended an invitation. For Gini, the prospect was irresistible: a long-lost cousin, the shared home city, an invitation on a super yacht, and a gala at the Opera Garnier— given her background as a violinist, it was an opportunity she couldn't pass up. She didn't expect a refund for checking out of the hotel early, just wanted Andreas to take her luggage down to the port.

Athena came around later that day, having slept off the previous day's activities, which included dinner and drinks on the *Sophia*. "It was love at first sight," she said, when Gini and Yanni, rather John, met. They exchanged life stories with each other and couldn't take their eyes off each other either, maybe even more.

Yanni had made it to Hollywood in the end after an arduous journey that had taken him first to his uncle's restaurant in Astoria, New York. He put in three months working long shifts as a waiter. Once he had enough to continue his journey to Los Angles, he was off, travelling by Greyhound bus across America. The journey had been at times exciting, boring, and on one occasion particularly terrifying when he was mugged near the bus station in Chicago. Yanni's plan was to go to film school to study film production. He had no thought of being an actor. However, after securing a job on a film set as a runner, just for the money, he was asked to step in when one of the actors developed a major fear of the horses being used in the film, which was based on a modern-day ranch in Arizona. Yanni had befriended the horse trainers on set. Like many locals on Hydra, he had grown up around horses and mules. The island, where motorised vehicles are sparse, heavily relies on four-legged transport. As luck would have it, Yanni also fit the profile for the actor's role in the movie, propelling him from a lowly "runner" to an "extra" riding horses.

Yanni, now anglicised to John, got a week's work on the film set, which then qualified him to join the Screen Actors' Guild. From there, things became easier. His looks and skills were in demand, and he found himself in the right place at the right time. He secured more film parts, each role bigger than the last. Within five years, he had mastered English, specifically American, and was landing minor roles opposite big stars. John's luck continued when he met a famous Hollywood star and producer with Greek connections and a fondness for Hydra. This "Hydra" connection boosted his career, and within ten years, he was starring in significant film productions. Yanni, now John Stephan, had made it, in no small part thanks to Sophia Loren and those photos that Athena's aunt Hera had treasured and her other aunt, Poppy, had taken many moons ago.

This was John's first visit back to Hydra since he had left all those years ago with the money he had squeezed out of Ute. He had planned to spend some time on Hydra, but after meeting Gini, he told Athena that, unexpectedly, he had returned to Hydra and found someone special he hadn't realised he had been searching for. So, he decided there was no reason to stay; he was leaving, and Gini was joining him.

And just like that, Gini was gone. Two days later, I watched the large blue and white super yacht pull up anchor and leave. Was that really Gini on the top deck staring back at Hydra? And who was that good-looking, expensively dressed man next to her? None other than Yanni, of course.

CHAPTER 38

T he season was drawing to a close. My first season on the island, and I had survived. Now it was October. Though I still had two pending court cases, which my lawyer, Condos, said would probably take place during the winter on the nearby island of Spetses. Condos would attend, saying, "And no need for you to be there, Zoe. In fact, best if you aren't because if the judgement goes against you, you could end up in handcuffs again," he laughed at the notion, finding the idea rather amusing.

The Greek summer residents had departed, returning to Athens, Paris, London, Geneva, or wherever their children attended school or where they ran their businesses. The tourists on the island during October were primarily British or Scandinavian, seeking warmth away from the colder northern climates.

Many local Hydriots were also preparing to leave, mostly heading to their apartments in Piraeus or nearby suburbs in Athens. Only a few hardened Hydriots, some expatriates, and those with no other options planned to endure the winter months on the island.

I, too, would be shutting down Martha's House for the winter. Bry had already left, saying he was absolutely coming back the next year, for a longer stay. My delightful Irish guest remained, diligently writing in his room. However, soon everyone, including him, would need to leave. I contemplated spending a few months in England, seeing my family in Marlborough and leaning on the hospitality of some London friends and catching up on sleep. Maybe, I considered, I might even winter in Ireland. The thought of visiting Dublin and spending some time with Padraig sort of cheered me. Initially elated at the thought of getting off the island for a few months, I was surprising myself at some of my reluctance. My memories of life in England were now in black and white. Whilst my life here in Greece was in full colour.

A few weeks later, Katerina and I finished closing up Martha's House. We stripped all the beds, scrubbed every corner, cleaned and stored the outdoor furniture, disposed of all rubbish, and finally closed the windows and shutters. Katerina agreed to drop by weekly to air out the place and ensure everything remained in order until my return. Additionally, as I had inherited the colony of Aunt Martha's cats that took residence at the back of the property; they'd need food and water throughout the winter. I bade Katerina farewell and, feeling surprisingly heavy-hearted, wheeled my suitcase down to the port, heading to Isalos café to await the hydrofoil to Piraeus.

Many were leaving the island that day, making Isalos bustling. I was practically elbow to elbow with patrons on both sides. Sneaking a glance to my right, I was struck by the profile of a particularly handsome man. He sported dark, slightly receding curly hair, tanned muscular arms visible under a tight polo shirt, and wore aviator sunglasses. As he began to turn towards me, I quickly averted my gaze, not wanting to get caught staring.

"Zoe, it is you, Zoe Miller, isn't it?" I turned back, unable to recall how he might know me. I was certain I'd remember him if he had stayed at Martha's House. He removed his sunglasses, and recognition dawned. Those distinct brown eyes were unmistakable. "Mihali, is that you? Oh my goodness, it is!" Mihali, my teenage crush that had ended abruptly when he invited me to his father's mansion to listen to music. Our rendezvous was short-lived; upon entering, his father, Manolis, had directed some stern words in Greek towards Mihali before essentially ordering me to leave. That embarrassing event from twenty years ago felt like just yesterday. "You've grown up, Zoe," Mihali remarked. And grown out in certain places I'd rather not have, I mused internally. "So have you, Mihali. What brings you to Hydra?" The skinny boy with glasses from my memory had matured into a striking, self-assured man. The thought of his father bossing him around now seemed improbable.

I didn't have to imagine, because Mihali started to tell me that his father Manolis had died a decade before Aunt Martha. His sister was running the family shipping business. To his father's disappointment, he wasn't interested in taking over from him and his sister was better at it anyway, he said. He was a yacht designer, based in Rome. He focused on sailing yachts using the best eco technologies. He had come to Hydra for a rest after a very busy year. He was going to oversee some repairs to the family mansion, before heading to Fort Lauderdale in Florida in two weeks for a boat show.

Mihali seeing the suitcase jammed up against Zoe's table, complete with a large name tag showing Zoe's name and address in Marlborough, England said "It's a pity you're leaving, Zoe. We could have had dinner together and caught up on old times."

"Leaving? I'm not going anywhere, Mihali. This suitcase isn't mine. Absolutely not. It belongs to a guest. I offered to bring it down for her since she wanted to shop before catching the ferry." Was it wrong to fib? It was a white lie, and surely everyone, even Aunt Martha, had indulged in one occasionally. "I would love to have dinner with you Mihali. I just need to leave this suitcase with George at the bar inside for my guest."

The case had mainly winter clothes in it, anyway; my Hydra wardrobe remained at Martha's House.

England and Ireland could wait a fortnight. Katerina and the colony of cats might be surprised by my sudden reappearance at Martha's House. Yet, with Mihali's return to Hydra and our coincidental encounter at the port, it begged the question: was it mere luck, or was it fate?

The End